Caz
EIGHTH
CHILDREN'S POETRY

RED FOX

A Red Fox Book
Published by Arrow Books Limited
20 Vauxhall Bridge Road, London SW1V 2SA
An imprint of the Random Century Group

London Melbourne Sydney Auckland
Johannesburg and agencies throughout the world

First published 1990
© Cadbury Ltd 1990

Set in Garamond by
JH Graphics Limited, Reading

Made and printed in Great Britain
by Cox & Wyman Ltd
Reading

ISBN 0 09 980300 3

Contents

Publisher's note

The poems in this book were chosen by a panel of judges which included poets, teachers and educationalists, from over 40,000 entries for Cadbury's 1989/90 National Exhibition of Children's Art. This year is the eighth in which there has been a poetry section and the final judges – Jennifer Curry, Chairman of the Advisory Panel, anthologist and author; Peter Porter, poet and literary journalist; Gareth Owen, poet, novelist and playwright; and Michael Rosen, children's author, poet and anthologist – were delighted at the great variety of material. They chose as outstanding the work of Lucy Barker, whose poems appear on pages 124 and 144.

Lucy Barker comes from Battersea in South London and is eighteen years old. She has a conditional offer to read English at Cambridge University and is currently taking her A levels. As well as writing poetry in her spare time, her hobbies include jazz and theatre going.

18 other children have had their work awarded silver medals by the judges. Their poems appear on pages 11, 20, 26, 28, 49, 50, 52, 62, 65, 67, 68, 71, 75, 90, 96, 120, 123, 135, 168. The poem by Kieron Mohindra on page 160 received a special mention.

The poems have been placed into chapters to give the reader the opportunity to compare the ideas of children from as young as six to mature seventeen year olds on just about every conceivable subject. All the illustrations are taken from entries to the Art & Design section of this year's Exhibition, and they complement the poems in an unusual and pleasing way.

We are very happy to be publishing such an interesting and original book and would like to thank all the writers and artists for their superb efforts. Don't forget, there's another chance to see your poem in print in the Ninth Cadbury's Book of Poetry to be published in 1991. For details on how to enter next year's exhibition please turn to page 187.

Foreword

Education is currently undergoing huge changes – the introduction of the National Curriculum, new methods of teaching, computerisation and high technology. These advances can seem daunting to adults – how many of us have offered to help with homework only to find that we are struggling to understand the most elementary problem!

However, it is almost a relief to find that what has not changed is the unique way in which children express themselves using the written word. Their hopes, dreams and aspirations are here amongst these pages, but because it is a book of children's poetry, you will also find many pages filled with thought provoking ideas that may even prick your conscience – about the environment, society, destitution and war. Young people of today have their fingers firmly on the pulse of life and it beats strongly throughout this book.

It is now eight years since Cadbury started publishing this annual book of children's poetry as part of Cadbury's National Exhibition of Children's Art. Each book is a tribute to the creative talents of young people and their teachers. This one is no exception.

Cadbury are delighted to be able to encourage creativity amongst school-aged children and I do hope you enjoy reading this book. As usual Cadbury donate all royalties to the Save the Children Fund.

F D Brooks
Managing Director Cadbury Ltd

Cadbury's Eighth Book of Children's Poetry

AWARD WINNERS – Poetry Section
43rd National Exhibition of Children's Art 1990/91

CADBURY'S GOLD AWARD FOR SCHOOLS

James Allen's Girls' School
London

CADBURY'S INDIVIDUAL GOLD MEDAL AWARD

Lucy Barker, Age 18
James Allen's Girls' School, London

CADBURY'S SILVER MEDAL AWARDS – POETRY SECTION

7 and under age group

Lucy Golding (7) St Cedd's School, Chelmsford, Essex
Rebecca Hughes (5) St Catherine's School, Camberley, Surrey
Rowena Lewis (7) Brington CP School, Brington, Northamptonshire
Sanchia Pitcher (7) St Catherine's School, Camberley, Surrey
Rebecca Thomas (7) Garth Junior School, Maesteg, Mid Glamorgan

8–11 Age Group

Emma Buckingham (11) Halesworth Middle School, Halesworth, Suffolk
Charles Romito (9) University College Junior School, London
Sian Saunders (11) James Allen's Girls' School, London
Marcus Throup (11) Sandiacre Cloudside County Junior School, Nottingham

12–14 Age Group

Rebecca Barr (12) Newcastle, County Down, Northern Ireland
Corinne Berg, (14) Newstead Wood School for Girls, Orpington, Kent
Abigail Gibbs (12) James Allen's Girls' School, London
Emma Walkey (12) Halesworth Middle School, Halesworth, Suffolk
Samantha West (14) Sevenoaks, Kent

Elaine Drainer (17) Glasgow

Helen Goff (15) Uxbridge, Middlesex

Peter Warren (17) Burnham Grammar School, Slough, Buckinghamshire

SPECIAL MENTION

Kieron Mohindra (14) The King's School, Canterbury, Kent

43rd Exhibition Tour 1990–1991

BIRMINGHAM – The Gas Hall, Birmingham Museum and Art Gallery
off Chamberlain Square, Birmingham B3 3DH   Tel: 021-235 3890
Friday 19th October 1990 – 23rd November 1990
Open Monday to Saturday 9.30 a.m. to 5.00 p.m.
Sunday 2.00 p.m. to 5.00 p.m.

GLASGOW – Collins Gallery, University of Strathclyde
22 Richmond Street, Glasgow G1 1XQ   Tel: 041-552 4400
Friday 30th November 1990 – 4th January 1991
Open Monday to Friday 10.00 a.m. to 5.00 p.m.
Saturday 12.00 p.m. to 4.00 p.m.
Closed Sunday
Closed 24th December – 2nd January inclusive

SUNDERLAND – Sunderland Museum and Art Gallery
Borough Road, Sunderland SR1 1PP   Tel: 091-514 1235
Friday 11th January 1991 – 15th February 1991
Open Tuesday to Friday 10.00 a.m. to 5.30 p.m.
Saturday 10.00 a.m. to 4.00 p.m.
Sunday 2.00 p.m. to 5.00 p.m.
Closed Mondays.

WARRINGTON – Warrington Museum & Art Gallery
Bold Street, Warrington, Cheshire WA1 1JG   Tel: 0925 444400/30550
Friday 22nd February 1991 – Friday 5th April 1991
Open Monday to Friday 10.00 a.m. to 5.30 p.m.
Saturday 10.00 a.m. to 5.00 p.m.
Closed Sundays and Bank Holidays

MAIDSTONE – Maidstone Museums and Art Gallery
St Faith's Street, Maidstone, Kent ME14 1LH   Tel: 0622 54497
Friday 12th April 1991 – Friday 17th May 1991
Open Monday to Saturday 10.00 a.m. to 5.30 p.m.
Sundays 2.00 p.m. to 5.00 p.m.

PORTSMOUTH – City Museum and Art Gallery
Museum Road, Old Portsmouth, PO1 2LJ   Tel: 0705 827261
Friday 24th May 1991 – Friday 28th June 1991
Open Monday to Sunday 10.30 a.m. to 5.30 p.m.

HEREFORD – Hereford City Museum and Art Gallery
Broad Street, Hereford HR4 9AU   Tel: 0432 268121
Friday 5th July 1991 – Friday 9th August 1991
Open Tuesday, Wednesday, Friday 10.00 a.m. to 6.00 p.m.
Thursday and Saturday 10.00 a.m. to 5.00 p.m.
Closed Sunday

Galleries, opening times, and tour dates subject to alteration

CADBURY'S NATIONAL EXHIBITION
OF CHILDREN'S ART

Organised and Sponsored by:

**Cadbury Limited
Bournville,
Birmingham.**

Just Cats

Lady Picklededooda

Lady Picklededooda
  is a suspicious cat.
She won't go away until
  she knows what's going on.
She arches her back
  when you stroke her.
I can see her going to the
  hairdressers and asking
  them to do her hair.

Sanchia Pitcher (7)
St Catherine's School,
Camberley, Surrey
(Silver Medal Award winner)

Tiger on the tiles

The cat that comforts the baby,
The gentle siamese lady.
The playful tabby kitten,
Born in last month's litter.
Climbing up the curtain,
All tame that's for certain.

BUT

In a few months time a demon rises,

As darkness falls o'er the land,
The striped tiger tom creeps out the door.
The glowing ember eyes of the tiger on the tiles,
As he throws back his head and roars.
On the wild wet roofs of the jungle grass,
He silently stalks his prey,
The blackhearted demon he becomes at night,
Will change when dawn brings day.

Anil D Boury (10)
North Cave Primary School,
North Cave, Brough,
North Humberside

Reflections

When my cat stares hopefully into the pond
She jumps back in amazement
She pads with her paw at the cat looking back
Her friend ripples away.

Then her head follows the goldfish round the pond
A fat one looks up at her
The goldfish reflects in her golden eyes
She blinks it away.

Jessie watches me cleaning my teeth in the mirror
I make faces at myself
She is muddled by her two masters
Bewildered she darts away.

She gazes at the blank television screen
And sees her kitten twin
Then I turn on *The Really Wild Show* and
I switch her twin away.

Daniel Brudney (9)
University College Junior School,
Hampstead, London

In the garden

Curving her sly body
In and out of the scarlet pimpernels
Moving cautiously
Not to disturb anything
Almost camouflaged in her deep cloud-blue skin
Her sharp pointed ears are all you can see
Weaving in and out of gold primroses, deep maroon
    snapdragons and trimmed carnations
Her padded paws treading carefully on crumbled earth
Curving her body to swerve round a tree
The bright blue sky shines down on her
She seems positively to know where she's going
She reaches her paws up to scratch on a tree
Doing it in exact timing.

Holly Hall (10)
St Mark's CE Primary School,
Talbot Village,
Bournemouth, Dorset

The cat day

The cat must
be lonely
with no one to
play with.
I am at school
Daddy is at work
And Mummy is busy.
Poor cat.

Katie Minton (6)
Edenhurst School,
Newcastle-under-Lyme,
Staffordshire

'*Teala Weed on the Floor Because She was Scared*'
Wesley Brown (6)
Hollywall Primary School, Stoke on Trent, Staffordshire

My Cat

My Cat
Eats my shoelaces,
It thinks
They are mousetails.

My Cat
Watches the fish tank;
We call it her television,
She watches the fish
Opening their mouths.

My Cat
likes to lie 'dead' a lot of the time,
Lying on her back,
With her legs in the air.

My Cat
Brings us presents,
Dead creatures
On the doorstep.

My Cat
Likes somewhere cosy and warm,
A bed – a cushion
Or my comfortable lap.

Alice Hawkes (9)
St Cedd's School,
Chelmsford, Essex

Black cat

The thin, black cat
Crouches,
Dragging its stomach across the ground.
Its eyes like marbles,
Beady and bright,
Shining in the sun.
Moving elegantly with its tail
Flipping backwards and forwards
   like a whip
Moving viciously,
Its whiskers pointed,
Twitching in the strong wind.

Katy Mackenzie (11)
All Saints' Middle School,
Sudbury, Suffolk

'Chloe'
Hannah Cook (8)
Mendham Primary School
Harleston, Norfolk
(Silver Medal Award winner)

Smokey

While watering the lettuce
some drowsy summer day,
Smokey, cat of namesake grey
arrives unannounced.
Pausing beyond the honeysuckle
to receive the friendly smile
that is her due.

She perches on the fence pole,
four feet bunched up, one for each corner.
Mother ties the ivy trails with bits of string,
Causes Smokey much amusement.
She follows the wandering threads
but cannot grasp their wavering form.
She is content to nibble a knot.

For gardening her curiousity abounds.
First she looks on and thinks you quite mad.
Then she slips between your feet
to accost your trowel.
Tiring of this she stalks a butterfly
that flutters by.

Peter Williams (14)
Anchorage Park,
Portsmouth, Hampshire

The dormouse

The dormouse is hibernating
He sleeps in autumn and winter
If my cat ever tries to get one
I just hiss at her
and say
NO!
NO!

Neil Ramsbottom (7)
Ridge Hill Primary School,
Stalybridge, Cheshire

'Armoured Rat'
Ben Pugh (16)
The Wakeman School, Shrewsbury, Shropshire
(Silver Medal Award winner)

Two by Two

Birth

Within the blood of the nettles
And the scorch of the sun
On a bed of plaited moss, you will find it.
Surrounded in dandelion sweat and apple sap
And a grassy green stain upon its spine,
It lies there, a bundle of bones in one heap.
The earth around it has the smell of coffee beans,
Freshly ground coffee beans.
In the background you can hear
The chorus of the cars climbing the hill
And the thud, thud, thud of the child's ball upon the
    ground.
Around the tiny cluster of veins and bones,
Are a thousand green needles
Threading the rain from tree to tree
And weaving cobwebs of willow silk.
The continuous drip of the clay rusty drain pipe
Is the lullaby for the baby rabbit.

Emma Buckingham (11)
Halesworth Middle School
Halesworth, Suffolk
(Silver Medal Award winner)

The fate of the school hamster

The cat ate it
No, the dog chased it
No, I left it in the garden
And a bird flew off with it
No, a robber stole it
No, a badger made a hole with it
I can't find that hamster, strange isn't it?

An elephant sat on it
No, my aunty flattened it
No, my dad swatted it
No, the rat got at it
No, it got squashed by the telly
No, it got squeezed by Kelly
I can't find that hamster, strange isn't it?

A fire burned it
No, a fan turned it
No, a guitar plucked it
No, a hen clucked at it,
No, a snaked hissed at it
No, a chopper just missed it
So can we buy a rat, and that be the end of that?

Katie Dale (8)
Storrington,
Pulborough,
West Sussex

The experiment

They filled me full of poison
With a needle, long and thin
They painted me with evil things
Where they had shaved my skin.
They made me smoke some cigarettes
Dripped shampoo in my eye
To see if I'd get cancer
To see if I would die.
Irradiated me for hours
Until I dropped down dead
If I survived, they gassed me
Or hit me on the head.
I have died a billion times
By cruel hands, trained and skilled
I am the helpless animals
'Medical science' killed.

Elena Barker (15)
Lomond School,
Helensburgh, Strathclyde

Red squirrel

Leaping as a dash of deep orange inferno!
Delicacy in its dance
over green (damp) limestone, dry stone walls.

In the Lake District I saw it
in a soft peat wood
of steep wet walks.
Overlooking Windermere
on a rainy day,
near an old ruined castle
with tall green pines
– it scuttled up one.

Gnome ears pricked up
with a tuft on the tip
like a sprig of fresh water.
And big globe eyes.

A gush of wind blew drops on our heads.

Swivelling its body,
jumping,
it clutched a nut and chiselled its teeth along the lines
to eat it.
Turned once again
and a tail flew down a hole.

And that's the only time I've ever seen one.

Robert Filby (12)
Halesworth Middle School,
Halesworth, Suffolk

The dog

On Monday I had a dog
The dog had a kennel
I could not get him in
Because he was too long
He was also too fat
And the kennel was too thin
I've decided to trade him in
And get a dog that fits the kennel!

Dorrinda Cooper (6)
Innisfree House School,
Wythall, Birmingham

'Fox in a Pine Forest'
Catherine Montgomery (9)
Bewdley
Worcester

Born to this world

He flopped out of his world into ours
to smell the earth like curdled tobacco.
One worm wriggled past his body, swollen.
He smelled the fresh dew, the crocheted cobwebs
and the sharp barbed wire.
He opened his unused mouth
and the first surprised whimper drifted out.
His first breath filled his lungs
with the sweet smell of rape
and the feathers of dandelion;
he felt the warm embracing tongue of his mother
and the beating of her heart had gone,
replaced by the discordant music of the birds, the bees
    and life.
But the warm churning of his mother's stomach soothed
    him.
And then, his mother's milk heated his inside
and filled him with a warm milky glow,
her low, baritone call smothering the sound of the world.
His legs were detached – and unusable
but he didn't know they were his, so why should he
    worry!
He lay his head on his mother's side
and her heart beat a lullaby
that rocked him to sleep.

Hannah Edwards (11)
Halesworth Middle School,
Halesworth, Suffolk

My dog

I have a dog
His name is Roland
I asked him to turn a record over
He ran away
Away to hide
And I still didn't hear the other side

Hayley Savage (7)
St Margaret's CE Infants' School
Warrington, Cheshire

Kamba

He shuffles and sways,
He plods along
His domed, patchwork shell
Swirls in hexagons.

His snakeskin head nodding
His black, beady eye searches for food,
He grins as he munches
Yesterday's wrinkled lettuce leaf.

His stout, scaly legs are awkward
He stumbles through his water saucer,
His toe-nails scratching the earth
Mole under the tangled straw.

Vanished! only the pencil end of a tail
And the heaving of the mound
Show us where he will sleep
The winter through.

Charles Romito (9)
University College Junior School
Hampstead, London
(Silver Medal Award winner)

A sssnake poem

I am a sssnake and my name isss Sssid
And I live on Ssst Patrick'sss Ssstreet,
I used to have a pet moussse but I ate it lasst week,
I go to the ssshops once a week,
My favourite food iss sssausssagesss,
And my favourite sssubject isss Englisssh.

Caroline Hoyle (11)
Hollymount Primary School,
Greenmount, Nr Bury, Lancashire

Frog

Frog leaps out of my hands
And slips into the water
His legs pulsing him down
Into green asylum, his
Small mind rejecting the
Faintly intimate greeting as
Another dangerous meeting
With death.

Peter Warren (17)
Burnham Grammar School,
Burnham, Slough,
Buckinghamshire
(Silver Medal Award winner)

'Bird on the Rocks'
Edward Montgomery (10)
St Mary's Primary School, Isleworth, Middlesex

Seals

See how he dives
See how he sings
See how the man is killing him.
Please, please stop.
No!
Said the man with the gun.

Claire Ives (7)
Ridge Hill Primary School,
Stalybridge, Cheshire

Otter

His whiskers comb the moonlight,
Where the frosted bank
Is a village of voles.
His skin is an oily plush.
A living bolt in the water,
He vanishes
Like a magician's assistant,
A reflection of mystic wonder,
Curving, curling,
A snake in the stream.
His slippery catch
Is still in a moment.

Ceri Whitham (11)
Debenham High School,
Debenham,
Stowmarket, Suffolk

Spiders

Spiders are hiders,
They hang on the ceiling
On a thin thread,
They go in your clothes
With eight little toes

SO!

Spiders are hiders.

Timothy Gray (11)
Woodland Middle School,
Flitwick, Bedfordshire

Look up

Look up   Look up
Over your head
It's a pterodactyl.
I thought they were dead
Way up   Way up
High in the sky
That's not a pterodactyl
That's just a fly.

Grant Gibson (6)
Broughton Primary School,
Edinburgh

The fly

The fly
Like an aerial tramp
Lands upon unwanted waste.
Dirty,
He skids drunkenly
Into a baker's shop,
His six grimy hands
Land on sticky buns
Left in the sun, slowly
Melting the sickly icing.
Tries to get up,
But stuck, heaves
And lumbers
Heavily
Into air.

Philip Clark (12)
All Saints' Middle School,
Sudbury, Suffolk

Bluebottle

Bulging eyes staring, fish-like;
Round fat hairy body,
Hairs soft like a cat's fur;
Veined wings, zebra stripes,
Hovers over sticky jam,
Buzzing and zizzing;
A little, blue alarm clock.

Ellen Gass (12)
Lady Adrian School,
Cambridge

The fly

His eyes are the windows to his soul.
His frail, pencil-sharpening wings
Catch the wind to make his flight
He sticks to the iced bun for his life
   And spits,
Sucks and goes.
A thief in action
Sometimes caught, he pays the penalty
Of his life.
He is a speck of shining velvet.
   A thief,
A thief in action.

Kirstie Leeming (11)
Halesworth Middle School,
Halesworth, Suffolk

Stick insect growing old

The family of stick insects grows larger
Their forest of privet grows green
The baby clings on to his mother's back
Camouflaged together with the rough stems and the
    soft leaves.

But the privet dries and dies
The stick insects' lives edge away
From soft green into stiffness
Does it feel strange, like getting arthritis?
Are they in terror of gnarling into bark itself,
Their life green draining into the sticks, and
    disappearing.

Now they are the harsh rough stems
Instead of new fresh leaves.
They are growing old.

Hannah Dawson (10)
Leeds,
West Yorkshire

Chick

Tilting slowly
Tilting fast
A nice smooth egg wobbles fast
Wobbles slowly
Dribbling a liquid,
    a nice tapping sound.
The chick sweats
The chick opens the shell.

Liana Fish (7)
Ridge Hill Primary School,
Stalybridge, Cheshire

'The Cock'
Christopher Marr (4)
Hardy Mill Primary School
Bolton, Lancashire

Taking flight

To feel that invisible force in
  my feathers,
That is what I want.
For weeks I have watched my
  parents,
Soaring on corridors of air.
Corridors which are to be my escape.

I look down,
It is a long way to the river
  below.
Must I put my trust in a force
  I can not see?

Yes I must, now.
I jump and my wings open,
I'm flying,
At last I can join my parents,
And rule the sky.

Paul Duley (15)
The Mountbatten School,
Romsey, Hampshire

Wren

He keeps time in a clucking tail feather –
Strutting to a fist fight his making –
keeping guard of the fortress;
The machine gun warrior.
Clicking tongue tripping upon itself.
Repetition on repetition.
Pebble stone supper
fuel for the song chatter.
He is the candle flicker
of the hawthorns

Gone and relit
in a second of video fast forward.

Stephen Routledge (14)
Rhydypenau School,
Llanishen, Cardiff

The Great Crested Grebe

The Great Crested Grebe with its head-dress on
  ready to go to the ballroom dance.
His body is a shiny silken cloth with a tinted
  brown shawl covering the silk on his back.
His beak is a dagger to warn off people not
  invited to the dance.
Some people do not take the warning – that's why
  his beak is stained red! with blood.
Now the king is hungry he goes out to find
  his meal.

Rebekah Appadoo (9)
Swinton Brookfield Junior School,
Swinton, Mexborough,
South Yorkshire

'The Crow and the Snail'
Natasha Davies (7)
Hayle, Cornwall

Seagull on the sands

Poor thing we said
It's ill we said
Helpless seagull on the sands
Tired and frightened we said
Sorrowful eyes we said
Stranded on the sand
It's dying, dying, dead we said
Sad we said
Upset because it's dead
Dying seagull on the sands.

Natalie Bannister (9)
Bedford Junior School,
Bootle, Merseyside

Peacock

A strutty, nutty peacock is
prancing ostentatiously on the lawn.
Attracting a female by proudly
displaying his multi-coloured plumage.
A strutty, nutty, corky, mosaic
Boss of the park.
A funny fellow is the peacock.

Jonathan Goldsmith (7)
Lincewood Junior School,
Basildon, Essex

A bat

A bat
Flaps like a rag
At night.

Matthew Rowland (11)
All Saints' Middle
School,
Sudbury, Suffolk

Monster

A prehistoric reincarnation
Reborn pterodactyl,
Like a broken umbrella,
Menacing, silhouetted against the sun.
Beak, edged with saw-teeth, gaping,
Screeching like a witch's cackle.
Eyes black, drilling down on the scrubland,
Fixing on a failure to hold a breath.
Swooping, talons splayed like a circle of
   thorns
To puncture the prey,
A trembling, bleating goat.
The bat wings droop
Like a black tent
Over the blood and bones.

Adam Wilson (11)
Rishworth School,
Ripponden, West Yorkshire

Tyrannosaurus Rex

Tyrannosaurus is so tall
He could even knock down
Our back wall.
He walks side to side
Because he is so wide.
He is as large as our garage
   roof.
I'm glad he didn't live in my day.

Luke Bass (7)
Newark,
Nottinghamshire

It's just another species

It's just another species,
It won't matter just this one.
It's just another species,
Soon to be gone.
Come on, men, be on your toes,
Sharpen the harpoon,
'Thar she blows!'

It's just another species,
So aim for his head,
Cut off both tusks,
As soon as he's dead.
Leave the body to rot in the heat,
The vultures and hyenas can have the meat.

It's just another species,
So club her on the head.
After all, she's worth nothing
Until she's dead.
Skin her carcass, let the snow
   stain red,
We don't believe a word the
   conservationists have said.

It's just another species,
What else can we slay?
It may be man that becomes the next
   prey.
After all, he's just another species . . .

Jane Hamill (11)
Fleetwood High School,
Fleetwood, Lancashire

As a Child

The journey

It's dark in here – it's warm and safe.
My very own space – for me to grow.
Inside this bubble, far away – yet very near.

I can hear the unceasing beat – beating for me –
    A rhythm soft and sweet.
I cannot see, or smell or taste . . .
But I can touch within my place.

My place is changing . . .
I'm squeezed and pushed –
What's happening now?
Confusion . . . fear,
My place is left behind.

This is a dreadful thing,
I'm pushing downwards,
The rhythm has all gone.
Where am I now?

The pushing stops . . .
I'm somewhere else!
This somewhere does not push me now.
I'm feeling free – yet still afraid.
My eyes are opening,
I see, I feel, new things are here.
A soft sensation, like my special place.

A gentle touch, a murmur soft and sweet.
Loving hands – these are my friends.
I am born –
I am loved –
I am me.

Caroline Scott (9)
Healey County Primary School,
Rochdale, Lancashire

'Man and Child'
Jody Barton (16)
Geoffrey Chaucer School
Canterbury, Kent

A aboot me.

I wis born in Scotland,
In the shire o Aberdein,
Nae far fae Fyvie Castle,
The finest iver seen.

I'm cad Isla Forbes,
I bide near Turra toon,
A'm affa gled I'm a Quine,
And nae a daft wee loon.

Ma faither is a jiner,
He uses different wids,
He maks doors and windies,
And sometimes things wi lids.

Isla Forbes (10)
Fyvie School,
Fyvie, Aberdeenshire

My nose

My nose
is little
and an
elephant's
nose is
big

An
elephant's
nose
can
lift
and
my
nose
can't

Christopher Cunningham (6)
Our Lady's Preparatory
School,
Crowthorne, Berkshire

Me

My hair grows long,
I like it,
Because in the dark
I can cwch it.
My bones grow strong
So I can open my sandwich box.

Sarah Broder (4)
Lodge Hill Infant School,
Caerleon, Gwent

'My Face'
Ummeia Pervez (5)
Military Rd Lower School
Northampton

My scream

From far away,
Down the sterile corridor,
A tiny cry comes.
A small murmur,
A whimper,
Develops a scream.
They are down there,
Smiling at the scream
Lovingly letting it fill them,
No thought of me.
I slide off my seat,
The sound of the scream
Still echoing through the silence.
My silence.
Slowly, I move,
Making my way
Amongst the mute hustle
That surrounds me.
Stretched, to my full short height,
I stare through the door
At the staring faces.
All eyes are focused
On the scream.
Slowly, my eyes lower towards it,
A small crinkled bundle,
Saturated in my mother's love.

Denise Daniels (15)
Ramsey Abbey School,
Ramsey, Cambridgeshire

Sulk

When I
am cross,
it is easy
for me to
get even
crosser.
I scowl
and howl
until
I am so
cross
that I
just
go on.
and behave
like a
maniac!

Nicholas Hodges (6)
St Anthony's School,
London

Rainforest

As a child
my granny's russet carpet
was an infertile forest floor,
shadowed by tall hardwoods –
furnished to house her clothes,
twisted tribal faces ingrained in the doors;
leafy walls crept towards the painted sky
where the sun,
hanging from its insulated vine,
shone for all its sixty watts' worth;
bright tropical flowers decorated the mantle,
their scent trapped within a porcelain glaze;
and strange birds,
(two in fact),
stared down from the wall –
I never once saw them move, though,
from their home in my rainforest.

Elaine Drainer (17)
Beardsen, Glasgow
(Silver Medal Award winner)

My room

My room is big and light and white
it kind of floats on top of our house
The room smells and feels of me
it's my room.
When I wake up in the morning to get up for school
the room is still sleeping
if I'm really quiet I can hear it snoring.
On Saturday morning the room wakes me up
with a long white finger down the back of my nightie,
it's not an impatient waking up like the ones that my
    Mum gives me
but a nice kind of sleepy yawn that says to me, 'Hi. It's
    me. Are you STILL asleep?'
and then my room laughs and I laugh too 'cause it's
    about twelve o'clock.

Sometimes my room helps me do my homework
it kind of says to me 'Are you worrying 'bout that
    homework? Don't bother.'
And then if I get really good marks in the work
and the teacher asks me who helped me I just smile and
    say 'No one.'
It would be pretty stupid if I said my room.

Rebecca Barr (12)
Newcastle, County Down,
Northern Ireland
(Silver Medal Award winner)

Phobia

My sister has a phobia,
It's not fair,
That Mum gives her something and not
  me,
Mum just told me that Julia had
  just got a phobia,
It must be in her room.
I will creep into her room now and
  get it,
I crept into her room and looked around,
I saw a horrible, black, ugly, creepy
  spider!
I ran screaming to Mum,
  she said I had a phobia too.
I ran upstairs thinking Mum must have
  put it in my room.
I'm still looking for it,
Maybe I'll find it tomorrow.

Laura-Jane Houghton (11)
Hadleigh, Benfleet,
Essex

Rhubarb crumble

Pink limp sticks
Sharp and sour.
My throat clogs up and won't let
  it go down.
Quickly I rush to the sink
but nothing happens.
My eyes start to water.

Rowena Lewis (7)
Brington County Primary School,
Little Brington, Northamptonshire
(Silver Medal Award winner)

I'm never ill

I'm never ill,
Never, ever.
I don't miss parties,
Never, ever miss school,
Never, ever have measles,
Nor chicken pox.
I'm only ill on a Tuesday.
I find spinach
Loathsome.

Christopher Daffin (9)
St Andrew's School,
Rochester, Kent

Feeling thirsty

Get back from the market
with me stuff,
feeling thirsty.
Out drops a mango
from me bag.
When me see it
me go mad.
Get out a knife,
no time to lose,
cut it in half.
See that nice juicy mango!
Down the throat it goes.
That juice tripples off me chin
and on to the floor of me kitchen.
Me don't care
about nothing else around me!
Just me mango!

Cecelia Thomas (10)
Grasmere Primary School,
London

Machines

Sewing machine
sews all day
it's got a pedal and wire
only press the pedal down
then it works
er er
goes all day long my mam
shouts
switch that off
but I just keep on sewing
and sewing
er er er er er er

Leanne Moffat (7)
Valley Junior School,
Whitehaven, Cumbria

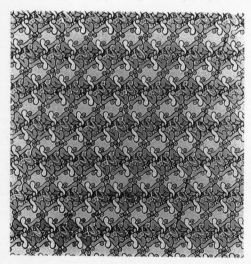

'After Picasso – Still Life on a Pedestal Table'
Jessica Watson (15)
Chenderit School
Banbury
Oxfordshire
(Silver Medal Award winner)

54

The keyboard blues

I wanted a keyboard on my birthday, but my mum said
    'No.'
I pleaded and pleaded but she still said 'No.'

I asked my dad: he said 'How much does it cost?'
I said 'Two hundred pounds.' He too said 'No.'

I went to my uncle: he asked what it could do.
I said it could play music. He also said 'No.'

I went to my grandad, sister and brother: but
I got the same answer. They all said 'No.'

As my birthday grew closer I went all tense.
I couldn't even get to sleep!

It was my birthday. I had just got back from school.
My mum said 'Son, I've got a surprise. It's up in your
    bedroom.'

I ran upstairs bursting with glee. It could be only one
    thing.
I opened the door. Guess what it was – a descant
    recorder!

Lalit Ghelani (13)
Garendon High School,
Loughborough, Leicester

I've got a lithp

Thome one pleathe help me,
I find it hard to thpeak.
My lithp ith tho incredible,
It getth worth every week.

Having a lithp ith no fun,
It can be embarathing.
It'th bad when you're talking,
But worth when you thing.

People thtop and lithten,
Thometimeth they even laugh.
When I'm being theroith,
They think I've made a gaff.

Thopping ith a problem,
When everybody thtareth.
The thop athithtantth look at me,
And thome don't theem to care.

They jutht thit and thtare at me,
Ath if I wath a rock.
Thometimeth they don't therve me,
Until I give them a thock.

Speaking rather upperclass,
Makes them think again.
They serve me straight away,
Is it some sort of game?

My lisp is now completely gone,
Many say that it's a boon.
But there are times I miss it,
And hope it comes back thoon.

Keith Howard (15)
Cramlington, Northumberland

'Monster'
Christopher Lloyd (4)
Abersychan
Pontypool
Gwent

Things I 'like'

'Like' is such a weak word.
It is in the same league as wobbly, feeble words
Such as 'nice' and 'quite' and 'sort of'.
They are the kinds of words that wibble and shake
Like a bowl of jelly.
These words are undecided and unprincipled.
These words have no manners.
These words, if human, would be cruel to those
    weaker and smaller than themselves,
      attempting to gain a sense of power,
Would take no interest whatsoever in world issues,
and above all, would loathe those with more intelligence
    and better upbringing than themselves.
These words I most certainly do not 'like'.

Things I LOVE
Love is a strong word.
It has passion, fire and power.
Strong words appeal to me.
They reach out to me with enticing fingers,
    and totally take me over.
I LOVE long, interesting words.
Words that I have to look up in the dictionary,
Words that jump off the page to seduce eyes, brain and
    mind,
Words that have a soul of their own,
Words such as versification, statuary and – whiffle.
Words that sound like music.
Words with double letters
These things I do not 'like'
but LOVE.

Jocelyn Andrews (12)
St Leonard's School,
St Andrews, Fife

I hurt myself

Blood running
Cut my finger bad
Brick
    Tripped
        Oops
Squished in the mud
Wet
Called
    Dale
Rain falling.

Tony Sulieman (7)
Denaby Main Infant
School,
Doncaster,
South Yorkshire

Operating theatre

Ramrodding double doors,
Flapping
Like waving hands
Farewell,
I slipped through a maze
Of fear
Into a deep, deep sleep.

Louise Morgan (11)
All Saints' Middle School,
Sudbury, Suffolk

Special treatments only

Inside the steel barrel
I watch the forces of gravity take hold
The door jams, my feet leave the ground.
The worst of my fears.
At five hundred revolutions my eyes drop out.
Water bursts up my nasal cavity
It burns like molten lead
How can I be involved in such depravity?
The steel holes grate my chin
And chip away my bone
The plastic bars which hold in the clothes
Swing round and deal me a thousand fatal blows.
My mouth fills up with soap solution
No time to worry about detergent pollution
The machine speeds up to one thousand, one hundred
    revolutions.
As I gargle cries of doomed despair.
I'm now pegged to the washing line
With the clean underwear.

Tim Rudgard (15)
The Mountbatten School,
Romsey, Hampshire

People Poems

Dad

Dad was someone who had everything
in the right place –
including his heart.
He never called us little terrors
He always called us the little ones or the kids.
He never hit us, but told us the reasons why
(when we weren't reasonable.)
He wore smart shoes,
comfortable trousers.
When you tried his shoes on
they were warm.
But when the time came for him to leave us
there was no warm feeling in the shoes.
No warmth or familiar smell in the clothing –
nothing.
And he left a gap in the word comfort   able.

Julia Wearn (11)
Sandiacre Cloudside County Junior School,
Sandiacre, Nottingham

Newspaper

At breakfast time,
Mother, me and newspaper,
sit at the table,
I often wonder,
What's behind it;
Last time I looked,
it was my dad,
but I don't know if it still is.
We slowly plough through
our scrambled eggs,
in silence.
But the silence is sometimes broken,
by the rustle
of pages turning in front of my face.
I see the headlines
flash by,
'Nurses demand pay rise!'
'Is Lawson the Ladies' man?'
What can be
so entrancing
about a newspaper,
I ask myself.
Sometimes I hear
the odd grunt or comment,
coming from behind
the mysterious pages.
Very rarely,
I see a hand grab
at a cup of tea,
take it behind
the black and white pages,
and put it back.

As I see the last page,
flick over in front of my eyes,
I become hopeful,
knowing that I will now get a glance,
of what's behind the newspaper,
I do,
but only for a short time,
there is always
another newspaper
waiting to be read.

Siân Saunders (11)
James Allen's Girls' School,
Dulwich, London
(Silver Medal Award winner)

My daddy

He has black hair,
And brown eyes.
He's got a watch,
And eyebrows.

Claire Harvey (4)
Lodge Hill Infant
School
Caerleon, Gwent

Memories – In Memoriam C.M.C.

In a room there is a desk,
In the desk there are three drawers,
In one drawer there is a tin,
And in the tin are memories.

I remember, or I think I do,
When a thing was nothing more than itself,
When something was hard, soft, big, small,
And when all you had to do was hold it.

I used to wake up so very early,
Lying just as I had when I was tucked up,
And still clutching Pooh, I tiptoed
Out of the door and sat by Daddy's head.

Soon he too awoke and kissed me, held me tight,
And wrapped me in my dressing-gown all pink, fluffy and
   white.

Beside his bed there was a desk,
In the desk there were three drawers,
In one drawer there was a tin,
And in the tin, still, there are memories.

Christopher Creissen (14)
The King's School,
Canterbury, Kent

They keep you fit and healthy

My mum is obsessed
By a book
By Adelle Davis
It's about food.

It's about lentils
And yoghurt
And brown bread
and greens.

They keep you
Fit and healthy
Says the book
By Adelle Davis.

Mum reads out extracts
At the table
And puts us off
Our food.

Abigail Gibbs (12)
James Allen's Girls' School,
Dulwich, London
(Silver Medal Award winner)

My mother

My mum waited patiently,
For Russ Conway to come
Into her life.
She paid sixpence for his record.
She wore flares and ski-pants.
They were the fashion,
1959 as it was.
So long ago,
Contained in this world,
I wonder,
Young, old, middle aged,
Can this be true?
Now she is in jeans,
and basketball boots,
And is in love with Phil Collins,
Paid one pound eighty for his record.

Alison Puxley (12)
Crestwood Community School,
Eastleigh, Hampshire

An Autumn forest

Towering trees stretching towards
the life-giving light,
Scattering down their leaves of red and gold,
Onto a dreary, dry Autumn floor,
Like an indulgent Sultan in glittering robes,
Handing out alms to the dutiful,
docile and defeated.

Nature ebbing and expiring
in the autumn forest.
Only the living creatures of the forests
know its secrets.
Its secret abundance of
fruitfulness.

The race is on!
The forest is alive with an
inaudible swarming, crawling,
hopping and buzzing.
Hunting, fattening, building,
storing.
A preparation for the coming
months of idleness.

Francesca Chiavarini (13)
James Allen's Girls' School,
Dulwich, London
(School Gold Medal Award winner)

Irritating poems

My Mum says
'You must not tell tales'
If you do she will SMACK.
When she is on the telephone
She says 'Be quiet.'
But when Edgar is at my house
She says sweeeeeetly 'Tea time'
Even worse, on the way to school
My sister sings

'Baaa Baa Black sheep have you any wool'

I prefer Michael Jackson

James Wood (7)
Dolphin School,
Hurst, Berkshire

Tact

Oh, you're such a wonderful mum,
Mum, do you know that I really love you,
You're just the best mum in the world,
What do I want?
Nothing, why do you ask?
I'm just saying that I like you,
Because you're much better than other mums.

Yes, I know I've never said it before,
Yes, and that I always say you're awful,
The worst mum in the world, yes,
But I was just thinking how nice you are,
OK, wonderful,
Yes, even fantastic,
Yes, yes, the best mum ever.
What do you mean?
No, I'm not in trouble,
Thank you, well actually,
No I have no bad news,
Well, not really anyway,
It's just that, well,
OK, don't rush me,
It's just that um,
I've just lost something,
It's just my little sister's watch,
Well, and her shoes and socks,
and her clothes and hair clips,
Yes, very careless and stupid,
And also mum,
I seem to have lost my sister.

Lucy Upward (14)
James Allen's Girls' School,
Dulwich, London
(School Gold Medal Award winner)

What a noise! What a racket!

What a noise, what a racket!
My mum gets cross when I open my crisp packet.
I scrunch it, and munch it, and crunch it
Until she shouts at me
'Don't make that racket!'

Every Friday morning,
When I am still in bed yawning,
With a rumble and a crash and a bang,
The dustbin men come bumping down our street,
And I shout,
'Don't make that racket!'

My sister has a radio in her room,
And every night it starts to boom,
Michael Jackson, A-ha, and Bros,
Makes such a noise that my dad shouts out,
'Don't make that racket!'

Simon Eastwood (7)
St Andrew's School,
Rochester, Kent

Neighbours

Next door kids go to that local school
And the mother goes shopping in her slippers.
Of course, you can instantly tell
What sort of family they are,
The sort that holiday in Majorca
On the other side it's no better
They drive a Lada,
And apparently, she's an alcoholic.

Over the road they 'co-habit'
Fancy name for hanky-panky
AND they don't wash their net curtains
At Number Twenty-Four they keep
Very odd hours, I can tell you, very odd indeed.

31 have a large, loud and uncontrollable dog
And a similarly inclined teenager.

Not really my sort of people
Are they?
Not a very sociable lot,
No nice dinner parties,
But what can I expect
An area like this
Still, since he died . . . .

I have a hollow space
in my thoracic cavity
Loneliness you say?
Yes, well, maybe . . . .

But why?

Helen Goff (15)
Uxbridge, Middlesex
(Silver Medal Award winner)

71

The dustcart

Here comes the dustcart,
Banging down the road,
Out climb the dustmen.
Walking past the cars,
One opens the gate,
And goes inside.
He picks up the dustbin bag
BEWARE OF GLASS!!
Almost cuts his knee,
Takes it to the dustcart,
CRUNCH!! CRUNCH!!
Off it goes to the dump.

Christopher Staples (7),
and Mark McDevitt (7)
St Cedd's School,
Chelmsford, Essex

'Self Portrait'
Rachel Collinson (11)
Albyn School for Girls
Aberdeen
(Silver Medal
Award winner)

My lazy sister

I get out of my bunk bed
'Get up Natalie!'
I get dressed
'Get up Natalie'
I eat my breakfast
'Get up Natalie'
I go and put my shoes on
'Get up Natalie'
Then I put my coat on
'Get up Natalie'
I come to school
'Goodbye Natalie you'll
be late for school again'

Melanie Hall (6)
Lincewood Infant School,
Basildon, Essex

Hungry fish

The fog wrapped itself around me.
The cold bit at my scarlet cheeks.
Ferociously, I squeezed my brother's hand.
Here, usually, energy would overcome me,
But in the mist I would surely get lost.
We foraged our way to the silver horse trough.
It housed our roach.
It was feeding time,
They were vicious
And they scared me.
My brother sprinkled golden crumbs,
Swished his hand timidly
Through the murky brown water.
A cry cut through the silence,
Echoed through the fog.
His hand rose,
Dripping fresh blood
Into the quivering wash.

Emma Davies (13)
Brandeston Hall School,
Brandeston, Suffolk

He who is never wrong

He hit me yesterday,
He who is never wrong
Hit me yesterday.
He thought I had borrowed his pen.
I hadn't.
I said, 'Have you looked under the bed?'
But he said that it would be
A ridiculous place
For me to borrow his pen
And so he didn't look there.
It was there, I know.
I hid it,
Just to see if
He who is never wrong
Could be wrong.
He was.

Samantha West (14)
Sevenoaks, Kent
(Silver Medal Award winner)

Gran and Grandad

'Good morning Karen
You look nice
Want a Polo?'
As they sit in their chairs drinking tea
Their room's all tidy
There's no noise
Not a biscuit in sight
Grandad's not allowed them
He was on dialysis
He still does gardening and my nan helps him
You can smell the sweet smell of the flowers
All around the room
And again my nan says 'You look nice, want a Polo?'
Then after the tea
My nan starts to knit
And all you can hear is the clicking of needles
And the snoring of Grandad.

Karen Hanson (11)
Meath Green Middle School,
Horley, Surrey

Granny

She twists it to the left,
She twists it to the right,
She pulls it,
She pushes it,
She shakes it,
She taps it,
She bangs it,
She bites it,
She levers it,
She ties her hanky around it,
She attacks it with her hair grip,
She throws it against the wall.
'Granny why don't you let ME open
your childproof pill jar,
It's much too difficult for you!'

Mark Booth (10)
Herne CE Primary School,
Herne Bay, Kent

'Mum and Mirror'
Elizabeth Peacock
(6)
Braehead Primary
School
Braehead
Forth
Lanarkshire

When I was your age

When I was your age, my child
I wouldn't have been so loud and wild
I would sit in the corner as quiet as a mouse
You wouldn't even know I was in the house.

When I was your age, my young lady
I would not leave my peas and gravy
I was made to eat every bit
For if I didn't I got a hit.

When I was your age, my little petal
There was no such thing as heavy metal
We danced to music by Brahms and Liszt
We did not jive or do the twist.

When I was your age, my flower
I'd go to bed at a suitable hour
And I'd never answer a grown-up back
For if I did I'd get a smack.

So my lass to you I'll say
It's lucky you weren't born in my day.

Jacky Foster (11)
Northmead County Middle School,
Guildford, Surrey

Poor old hat

I was looking in the garage last night.
An old scruffy hat I saw –
No use any more.
I took it from its shelf, torn and rotten.
I thought of all the days it had been on the head of
   Daddy
54 miles with a number on the front.
A ribbon round,
All so black,
Many years old.
Before my Daddy it was his Daddy's hat.
He used it every day for work
Like a cat, a faithful friend.
A smart black hat
No use any more.
Poor old hat.

Susannah Brough (8)
Greycotes School, Oxford

Grandad

The Grandfather clock chimes three o'clock.
I watch Grandad struggle to stand,
like a newly born foal.
His wrists turn a greyish white
as he increases the pressure on the dust
engraved windowsill.
He shuffles forwards towards the kettle
and flicks the switch.
The kettle jumps into life.
The windows stream with moisture.
The kettle whistles an F major scale,
as Grandad waits.
Cold ceiling cracks are stained with nicotine,
The table edges, showing splinters
like sharp daggers clustered around a magnet.
The curtains are smeared by tobacco smoke.
A goblet rests on the fireplace,
Pens crammed in . . . letters, post cards . . . years of
    memories.

Eugene Collins (11)
Halesworth Middle School,
Halesworth, Suffolk

My Grandad

Grandad Lea
Was getting old.
He's gone to Baby Jesus
To help him do his stuff.

Matthew Lea (4)
Lodge Hill Infant School,
Caerleon, Gwent

There's a girl in our rugby team

There's a girl in our rugby team
she's rough and tough and mean
she's tougher than the boys
she scores lots and lots of tries
and she tackles hard
she still sits in a corner and plays with dolls
when no one else is there
But when she's got her rugby shirt on
opposition beware.

Richard Craddock (9)
Earby County Primary School,
Earby, Lancashire

Hidden talent

There is a plain, white cupboard.
He sits in the corner, facing the wall so his doors can't
   open.
His contents would shine if the doors were opened.

He often wonders what would happen if the doors were
   opened.
He has faced the wall all his life,
So instead of shaming himself, he remains in the corner.

Many people see this cupboard facing the wall.
They wonder what is inside,
Think that as it does not show its contents it has nothing
   to show,
And leave it in the corner, alone.

A woman is curious.
She decides to look inside the cupboard.
She turns it around with difficulty and tries to force it
   open.
The cupboard is not sure what he should do.
The woman perseveres and the doors open.
She sees a brilliant light no one has seen before.

Matthew Odgers (14)
The King's School,
Canterbury, Kent

The mirror

She walks towards me
and, with dull eyes, glances at me
seeing what she really is.
I am lifted up and brought down.
But swiftly
I shatter in several places.
And, as I watch from scattered positions,
I am drawn smoothly across the smooth neck
as though I am a zip,
and pull the skin apart.
Again I am dropped
but this time she follows me
covering me with her body.
All there is, is blackness, helpless guilt
and oblivion.

Phillip Rigby (14)
Acklam Grange School,
Middlesbrough, Cleveland

An alley scene

The moon slashed through coal black clouds
Like a hot knife through rotting butter
And at that moment nothing moved
Except rats along the gutter
Along the streets the pushers walk
With their pills and with their gains
And in a room not far away
Someone puts heroin down their veins

I am the plague that stalks your world
I am disease and pain and rot
And unlike others upon your plains
I cannot be maimed or stabbed or shot
I am the symbol of want and greed
I am the spirits of gloom
I am Apocalypse itself
My only name is doom

Paul Carroll (11)
St John Vianney School,
Coventry, West Midlands

Drug addicts

Don't be a fool,
Stick to the rule,
Listen to this message,
And just act cool,
It ain't no joke,
So don't sniff coke,
Don't be an alchie,
And please don't smoke,
One glass of vodka,
And you'll be drunk,
One shot of drugs,
And you'll be sunk,
With the fastest drug dealer,
You'll be booked,
Please stop now,
Or you'll be hooked,
If your lung you love to singe,
Or take drugs with a dirty syringe,
You'll end up,
In a hospital bed,
With thirty two tubes,
Running out of your head,
So don't be a fool,
Stick to the rule,
Listen to this message,
And just act cool.

Asha Ghusar (13)
Woodside Secondary School,
Glasgow

Untitled

Unfinished houses
In an unpaved street.
Under the streetlight
Where the homeless meet.
Uneven railings
Hide an unused park,
Where unwanted canines
Uncannily bark.
An unfaithful wife
With an unstable mind.
Her unlucky husband
Unsure what he'll find.
Unemployed books
On an unlisted shelf,
A boy, too unlettered
To read to himself.

A uniformed gentleman,
With unnoticed dread,
Enters unsurely,
But the people have fled.
He looks round uncertainly,
Breathes in unclean air.
An unfit society
Is what he sees there.
This man, uninvited,
Unlocks a door.
The unmentioned past
Unfolds now once more.

The unprepared people,
Unsure what they'll meet,
Are only confronted
By their unhappy street.

Sarah Cohen (13)
Ealing, London

'*Bright Lights Bad City*'
Caroline Campbell (16)
Kilgraston School
Bridge of Earn, Perthshire

The vicissitudes of Mrs Woman-in-shoe and her amazing multitudinous offspring

'There was an old woman who lived in a shoe,
With so many kids she knew not what to do.
She gave them some broth without any bread,
Then whipped them all soundly and sent them to bed.'

But alas for the woman who lived in the shoe,
In these modern times such things you cannot do.
One lad shopped her to the RSPCC
And they sent round a young man to have a look-see.

He said 'Listen up, Mrs Woman-in-shoe,
Our Esther has tortures for people like you.
She'll stick you in jail, where horrors are rife
And then, worst of all, you'll go on *That's Life*.

'That's how it generally works nowadays
For people like you with your child-beating ways.
So beware, Mrs W, just wait and see,
Or your crimes will be broadcast on national TV.'

'I'll be good, I'll be good,' she cried out in fear,
'And I'll never again hurt my children so dear.'
And she didn't, in fact, or at least not too much –
Just the odd kick, shout, cuff, thump, wallop or punch.

But there were other probs for our Woman-in-shoe:
Her over-age kids were then noticed too
By the DHSS, that old bunch of hacks,
Who thought she was defrauding on her Poll Tax.

They therefore came round to survey the shoe-home
And assessed each young tot for its annual income.
Then they turned to the woman, smiling with glee
And said 'Six thousand one hundred pounds, fifteen pee.'

She couldn't pay this of course, needless to say,
And decided to sell up and then move away.
All over the country she therefore did roam,
In desperate search for the right kind of home.

The bungalow slipper in London looked nice
But was too dear, as was the huge welly in Fife.
A stiletto in Oxford? Too expensive indeed.
She was left with a dirty grey trainer in Leeds.

A mighty sad come-down for her, you might say,
But she and her family kept working away.
Their fortunes were slowly but surely restored
And in time they bought back the house they adored.

They are happy again now they live there once more,
And keep two cats, a budgie and Hush Puppies four.
With plenty of cash things are no longer Spartan –
It's a right happy life in that great black Doc Marten.

So take heart from the story of Woman-in-shoe
If things always seem to be getting at you
Whatever the problem you surely can win it
Provided, of course, you don't put your foot in it.

Euan Lees (16)
Hutchesons' Grammar School,
Glasgow

Give way!

Learner driving
Lorry speeding
Learner slowing
Lorry indicating.

Learner indicating
lights showing
green going
red showing

Learner stopping
Lorry crashing
police coming
ambulance rushing.

police arresting
learner dying
ambulance sounding
instructor flaring

Families worrying
court discussing
prison waiting
doctors helping.

Rebecca Thomas (7)
Garth Junior School,
Maesteg,
Mid-Glamorgan
(Silver Medal Award
winner)

You!

You!
Your brain is like a speck of dust.
You!
Your legs are stubby and fat.
You!
Your hair is like a mop.
You!
Your money is glued to your pockets.
You!
Your clothes have been dragged through the sixties and
    back.
You!
Your mouth is like a gaping railway tunnel.
You!
Your head is full of crawling maggots.
You!
Your arms are like lamposts.
You!
Your nose is like a corn-on-the-cob.
You!
You're about as reliable as a Delta bus.
You!
Your feet are the size of a chestnut tree.
You!
Your fingers are like rats' tails.
You!
Your breath smells like a cow pat in the summer.
You!
Your ears are like a pixie's.

Debbie Simpson (14)
St David's Secondary School,
Middlesbrough, Cleveland

Stephanie Jane

I see a patch of grey,
A concrete city beneath,
I'm looking down on a town
The people, out of reach.

I glide past into countryside,
And grab at tufts of air,
I look at sun-tanned fields,
None the worse, for years of wear.

I drift out even further,
Out into the roughened sea,
This whispering witness holds secrets,
But has no time to talk to me.

I continue rambling further
A mass of polka-dots below,
They've travelled far to get here,
They've even further to go.

I plummet down towards these vessels,
Live, and kicking, breathing air,
The sails plunge right through the wind,
A sense of competition is there.

I zoom in on one of the hundreds of ships,
It's called the *Stephanie Jane*,
Not old, not new, not lavish, not cheap,
But wilfully bearing the strain.

On deck is a man, staring ahead,
Damp and worn from the cold,
His eyes, they gaze, loving and warm,
His face is wise and bold.

I rummage in his pocket,
I find a picture, in a frame
It's of a little girl,
Whose body is twisted and lame.

And I journey, into this man's heart,
And scratched into it is her name,
A name he loves and cares for,
The name is 'Stephanie Jane.'

The expectancy in his mind, is great,
He's been gone, a very long time,
And although he may finish, first or last,
She's waiting, at the finishing line.

Alison Everett (13)
Millais School,
Horsham, West Sussex

Silhouette

If you were a
silhouette
I wouldn't know
the colour of
your eyes
or hair.

Chantelle Frost (6)
Our Lady's
Preparatory
School,
Crowthorne,
Berkshire

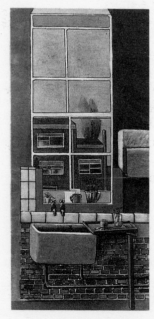

'The Art Room Sink'
Rushnah Cassim (12)
Nonsuch School For Girls
Cheam, Surrey

School Blues

Almost new

The train stops.
Several girls in the same
Uniform slowly disembark
The station clock reads:
   8.13
Nervous people rushing everywhere

The walk to school.
A large green caterpillar
Makes its way up the hill
The girl's watch reads:
   8.32
Nervous people rushing everywhere

Registration.
The basic rules are being
Explained as the bell rings
The clock on the wall reads:
   9.15
Nervous people rushing everywhere

The end of the day.
The bell echoes, chattering girls
Heading for their classrooms
The school clock reads:
    15.41
Relieved people rushing everywhere.

Kay Bradshaw (11)
Newstead Wood School For Girls,
Orpington, Kent

There's someone in our class . . .

There's someone.In our class who cannot.
Write in sentences our.Teacher keeps saying
write.In decent sentences a sentence is.
A group of words that makes complete.Sense.
But this.Someone never.Listens !

Their's somion inn or clas ho canknot spel proupirlei.
He as the mosst auful spileing nowlidge.
Mrs Catlledinner ses it's dubble ditch.
But thiss somion niver lissteenss !

There'ssomeoneinourclasswhoneverleavesafingerspace
betweenwords.MrsCastledinedoesnotapproveofhiswriting.
Shesayshemusthaveverythinfingers.
Butthissomeoneneverlistens!

There's someone in our class
who writes too big.
He tries to write small
but he hasn't got the knack yet.
This someone is a very small person –
not like his writing !

There's someone in our class who cannot concentrate.
This someone finds it very difficult to . . .
'What was I saying ?'

Marcus Throup (11)
Sandiacre Cloudside County Junior School,
Sandiacre, Nottingham
(Silver Medal Award winner)

Time

A day at school
seems years
and a day at home
goes in a flash.

Jeffrey Sargant (9)
South Green Junior
School,
Billericay, Essex

The watch

Bleep Bleep
A watch is going
Bleep Bleep
It doesn't give a toss
Bleep Bleep
It's getting louder
Bleep Bleep
Mr Gardner's cross!

Jens Niedzwiedzki (10)
Utterby County
Primary School,
Near Louth,
Lincolnshire

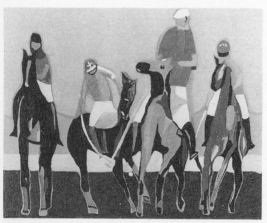

'The Game'
Noushin Dowlatshahi (13)
City of London Freemen's School
Ashtead, Surrey

Christmas joy

The audience, chilled from the frosty night
Fumbled into the stuffy hall.
Silver stars clung,
Tinsel was drooped around the crammed room.
They sat, not knowing what to expect
From a group of children wearing old curtains
And tinsel round their heads.
The hall grew warmer,
A light beamed on to a home-made crib.
A cloth was draped over Jesus' worn face.
Backstage everyone was excited,
Except me.
Hot and clammy, I sat in a corner
Waiting for my turn.
I was pushed on to the stage
And blinded.
My angel's costume was crumpled,
My face was numb.
I could see the Headmaster
Lounging in his plastic chair.
He gave a smile,
Urging me to speak.
One eye gave a friendly wink.
It was Christmas.

Helen Robinson (13)
Brandeston Hall School,
Brandeston, Suffolk

I like acting

I like acting,
And in my drama lesson
I can pretend to be a mother
scolding her child,
A teacher marking books,
A child who behaves badly,
A nosy housewife,
A person in pain,
An old lady,
A snob,
A bully,
Or a bully's victim.
I think I'm good at acting,
And my teacher agrees.
She says I have a natural talent,
For acting the fool.

Emma Slater (12)
Windsor Park Middle School,
Uttoxeter, Staffordshire

Something out of my head

I do not like writing poems.
When I went to school my teacher said
'Write a poem. Write something out of your head.'
I do not like writing poems
So I did mathematics instead.

Stephen Williams (7)
Velindre Primary School,
Brecon, Powys

Mie wurst leson

Sylentee warkin tyred an fedup
cachin old ov frends,
gripin tietly ontoo mie bag.
the ony fing ieye wory about izWo   rk.
Redd ,bloo,gren and yello tekst buks,
four most subgects lowe graeds.
(I wunder wy ?0.)
Apear on mie wurk.
Wel hear gose two mie ferst lesun,
Ingullissh.

Joanne Nicholls (12)
Llanrumney, Cardiff

My teacher

My teacher says my work is not neat.
My teacher says I haven't got the right pen.
My teacher says I haven't got my P.E. kit.
My teacher says I haven't done my homework.
My teacher says I make a lot of mess
My teacher says I am very fussy
My teacher is quite fussy herself.

Anju Kaul (9)
Tudor Middle School,
Southall, Middlesex

Trina Pain and Co.

Stepping out into the playground.
You know what's going to happen.
Little Trina strikes with her army,
Never to let you go.
'Mud game' she said,
with a grin on her face,
'I will get you yet.'
'The aim of the game is to sit you in the mud.'
I sprint down the playground,
Just in time to get caught.
Then when all is well they grab you
by the coat,
and then SPLAT!
right in the mud.

Ross Bellars (11)
Eynesbury CE School,
St Neots, Cambridgeshire

The real bully

Why does he REALLY do it?
  I REALLY don't know.
Personally I hate him.
  I REALLY do.
He's REALLY bad to people.
  I REALLY think so.
He REALLY pushes people around,
  That's what I don't like
I just wish he could be –
  Well I'm not being nasty
but I would REALLY enjoy it,
  If I saw him bashed around.
  I REALLY would
  By someone HUGE
REALLY, REALLY H–U–G–E.

Paul Robinson (12)
Colmer's Farm Secondary School,
Rednal, Birmingham

Ten happy schoolgirls . . .

Ten happy schoolgirls went down a mine,
 One slipped and broke her neck.
  Now there are nine.
   Nine happy schoolgirls skating round a plate,
    One missed her footing. BANG!
     Now there are eight.
      Eight happy schoolgirls all aged eleven,
       One had a heart attack,
        Now there are seven.
         Seven happy schoolgirls eating pic'n'mix.
          One choked on a crunchy wrapper.
           Now there are six.
            Six happy schoolgirls all still alive,
             One fell down a man-hole,
              Now there are five.
               Five happy schoolgirls lying on the floor,
                One fell through it.
                 Now there are four.
                  Four happy schoolgirls frightened of a bee.
                   Then the bee stung one,
                    Now there are three.
                     Three happy schoolgirls watching Winnie-
                       the-Pooh,
                      The TV exploded.
                       Now there are two.

Two happy schoolgirls went to Bonn
One got lost.
Then there was one.
One lonely schoolgirl, heart weighs a
ton.
Wandered into the distance.
Now there is none.

Rosemary Riley (11)
Sheldon, Birmingham

'My Friend Jennifer Reading'
Lyndsay Rowlands (9)
Daven County Primary School
Congleton, Cheshire
(Silver Medal Award winner)

Quarrel

He didn't call for me on the way to school,
I played with somebody else.

I sat with someone else in assembly,
He looked upset but angry coming out.

I found a felt pen mark on my English book,
I put biro on his jumper.

I nudged him so his pencil slipped,
He nudged me and my pen slipped.

He fouled me in soccer,
I belted the ball at him.

He put yellow paint in my red,
I put yellow in his black.

I think he poked his tongue out at me,
I gently touched him.

He walked home with me as usual,
I called for him to see if he would play.

Jeremy Consitt (11)
Bishop of Llandaff High School,
Llandaff, Cardiff

Time Off

The mountain

It was my birthday
I was six
my dad and I
climbed to the top
of the mountain
The car looked tiny
   Dad wanted to give up
   I didn't
When we got to the top
I said 'yippee'
Then we climbed
back down

Thomas Lloyd (6)
Abersychan,
Pontypool, Gwent

The hill was steep

The hill was steep,
So steep I could not climb it.
I tried and I tried
But I could not do it.
So I came down for a rest.
I think going down is best.

Raj Tanday (8)
St Andrew's School,
Rochester, Kent

We should 'ave stayed at 'ome

Cases packed, taxi waits
Happy now we've booked these dates,
Airport clear, board the plane,
Two hours later land in Spain
Luggage claimed, board the coach,
Driver takes us to the coast.
Reach reception, take room keys
Holiday starts and we are pleased.

Our room is on the seventh floor.
Lift is broken, what a bore!
Cases seem to grow in size,
As each floor number greets our eyes.

Room is found, we open door
Water greets us on the floor,
Plumbing's leaked and filled the room,
Expressions change from smiles to gloom.
Lights don't work, we're in the dark
Think we've booked in Noah's ark.

Turn around, down we go,
Join the turmoil down below,
Reach reception on our knees,
Asking for a new room, PLEASE!
'No rooms senor'
We stare in fright
So in the bar we spend the night.
Morning comes, it brings the rain,
How glad we are we've chosen Spain.

Alison Mangan (14)
Alun School,
Mold, Clwyd

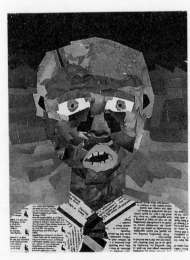

'Me, Myself and I'
Robert Streeten (12)
Holmewood House School
Tunbridge Wells, Kent

It's not far now

I was walking and walking.
It's not far now . . .
The sun shining glowing
Yellow and orange,
As hot as could be.
It's not far now . . .
A slight wind caught my
Face,
I breathed deeply enjoying
It while I can.
I want to stop.
It's not far now . . .
I picked at the brambles
And watched them melting
In my hand.
I moaned as we went up
And down hills.
Mostly up.
It's not far now . . .
How far's not far . . .
Not far . . .
Dad, you've been saying
That for the last three hours.

Louise Richardson (10)
Canon Pickering Junior School,
Harleston, Norfolk

The alley behind the chemist's

There's an alley where me and my mates go
Behind the chemist's at Carner Street
It's nothing special just a few old dustbins
and empty wooden crates, but it's
our alley, our private place where we can
play cars or tag
If you come near it Big Midge will
get you

It's much better than home
there's no privacy at home just disturbance
only me and my mates know
where it is
don't tell anyone

Hannah Ford (11)
Bishop of Llandaff Church in Wales School,
Llandaff, Mid Glamorgan

On the swing

I climb on to a rough seat.
I zoom up.
My legs are forced off the ground.
    Then my legs come
bombing back.

George Fisher (7)
Brington County Primary School,
Little Brington, Northamptonshire

Sitting on the balcony

Sitting on the balcony,
in the chair,
with my feet up,
head down,
with my watermelon,
munching away.
See the houses
with people popping out
of the window
for fresh air.
The trees swaying about
and the blue sky
like the river.
But all I want to do is
munch the watermelon
on the balcony.
My feet up,
my head down, eating my watermelon.
The cars go past and all the dust floats up.
But I don't care
as long as
my watermelon is OK.

Nazmun Nahar (10)
Grasmere Primary School,
Stoke Newington, London

On my bike

Two turns on the pedals and
I'm off on my own,
Getting faster and faster,
Speeding down a hill at a
thousand miles per hour,
The world whizzing past me in
a flash.
The wind in my face stinging
me like lots of little needles.
My hands feel numb against
the handlebars.
I feel freezing on the outside
but hot and sweaty on the
inside.
I feel tension building up inside
me as I jump over a bump and
cling on to the handlebars for
dear life.
I come to a rough surface,
the ground is spitting stones
at me as my wheels crunch
through the gravel.
I screech on my back brake,
skid around and brace myself
to go up again.

Thomas Hollett (11)
RA Butler Junior School,
Saffron Walden, Essex

The 75-metre hurdles

In the changing room
The atmosphere is
Tense.
Then,
Out on the track,
The speaker calls the competitors forward:-
The throbbing heart,
The feeling inside,
As if you're not
Really there.

Then it's
GO
And everything is up to you,
You can't let anyone down.
Strain ahead to the finish line.
Remember the technique,
Five strides;
Right, left, right, left, right;
Over the first hurdle;
five strides between,
And on.
Over twelve hurdles:-
Feet pounding,
Pushing,
Reaching,
Jumping.
The next hurdle in sight.
Keep going,
Then it's past
And another is ahead.

Keep leg inside,
Left arm tucked in,
Right arm flies out,
Touching left leg;
Over and down.
Must keep counting strides,
One
Two
Three
Four
Five
The last hurdle,
And it's
Reach for the finish.
No more obstacles,
The end is in sight.
Give of my best.
Run! Run! Run!
The end is here
It's gone
I've won.

Rachel Knowles (15)
St Martin's School,
Solihull, Birmingham

Illusions

The golden sand,
Hiding pink and brown shells
Children running,
Laughing,
Throwing beach balls to each other.
The waves,
Crashing against rocks,
Sending up showers of spray that
turn to gold as they are pierced by the Sun.
Then over come the clouds,
Dark and grey,
Lightning, rain, thunder.
Wonderful effects my keyboard has . . .
Really makes you think.

Joshua Hammond (9)
Leftwich, Cheshire

'Tears for the Sea'
Lucy Campbell (12)
Kilgraston School
Bridge of Earn, Perthshire

Being stuck in goal

The goalie's ill,
Oh drats I'm in goal.
Just my luck.
I've got the wind blowing in my face,
The ground's water-logged and it's near enough snowing.

All the play has been at the other end.
My hands are like ice cubes,
I feel the bitter weather,
Biting off one toe at a time.
Only a few minutes left,
And,
Suddenly,
They break,
Their best player is leading the attack,
He's shooting,
I summon up all my energy and hurl myself across the
    goal,
Landing with a thud,
It knocks me breathless but I'm still clutching the ball,
Everybody was bundling me,
The team's hero.

Paul Oliffe (11)
South Green Junior School,
Billericay, Essex

'Fore'

I drive off from the first tee,
A score of under ninety would be great for me.
At the 6th hole I land in a dip,
But clip it out with a brilliant chip.

Unfortunately at the 9th, I land in a bunker,
I play a wedge out, I can't believe it, I've sunk her.
But suddenly things take a turn for the worse,
I rant and rage and begin to curse.

I hook and slice my way through the rough,
I'm losing strokes, but that's just tough.
I must be calm and keep my cool,
In golfing, that's the golden rule.

At last I'm on the 18th green,
The clubhouse can be clearly seen.
And when the final putt is sunk,
It's off to the clubhouse to get drunk.

Andrew McIntosh (14)
Bearsden Academy,
Bearsden, Glasgow

Fishing

The float goes under
my eyes pop out
my mind is in a whirl
as I reel it in
   and in
   and in
  and in
  and in
 and in
and in

this big.

Richard Hemstock (10)
South Green Junior
School,
Billericay, Essex

'Behind the Times'
Charlotte Morgan
(13)
Welshpool
Powys

The dream of fisherman

Feathers fall into the surf
And fur the sea with mould like dust.
The mesh of silver is mercury,
Penetrating the depths into organized squares . . .
Green fishes' scales in a wax currency,
Overlap, like the waves overlapping.
A flick of a tail becomes
A blue flame, dancing in the dark,
Mosquitoes clouding like fishes' eyes
Staring into my own
As they flounder in the nets,
Like spider web.
The white horses gallop into
Steaming white smoke or chalky swirls,
Chalk like the cliffs,
That crumble into my mind,
White against black,
And the fish become ribbon,
Knotting the net as it battles the surf,
Which is hair flooding from my shoulders.
As I run into the skyline,
Panic streaks the sky, orange juice,
Squeezed from the Sun
Which swallows me in its sheets of blue nightmare.
The sea is not the sea.
The land is not the land.
All is a huge fish,
Which lands, still alive on my plate,

And gives a last wriggle before
Packing its bags and leaving,
To break the wave pattern with the alarm
Of my clock.

Emma Walkey (12)
Halesworth Middle School,
Halesworth, Suffolk,
(Silver Medal Award winner)

Fishing

Spinning for pike is dangerous
But exciting.
You cast out
A bite!
Then strike
And reel in.
See the silver spinner spinning round and round.
Then there's a struggle
Get it on the bank.
Open its mouth with the gag
Take out the spinner.
A big mouth, a green body and sharp teeth
Fling it back.

Christopher Sansom (10)
William Shapland Middle School,
Tiverton, Devon

Wrestling

It comes on on Monday night
André the Giant, What a sight

The Rockers get kicked out of the ring
By Randy Savage the Macho King.

Double axe handle by Demolition Smash
The Powers of Pain go out with a crash.

Mr Perfect never been beat,
Hulk Hogan says 'You're dead meat.'

A drop kick by Honky Tonk Man
Tito Santana goes out with a slam
A big big punch by Bad News Brown.
Rowdy Roddy Piper goes right down.

Drop kick by Jake the Snake
Out of the ring goes The Earthquake

Three bells go, end of the match
Hulk Hogan wins. What a thrash!

Wesley Mee (11)
Garendon High School,
Loughborough, Leicestershire

The stamp collector

He hoards them like nuts.
Obsession captures
The little dark room
In unwary light.

The dust lies thick on
Each leathery tomb;
The magnifying glass
Focuses sight.

A new treasure placed
Enjoyment departs:
They are left forgotten
In paper graves.

Corinne Berg (14)
Newstead Wood School for
Girls,
Orpington, Kent
(Silver Medal Award winner)

Bowling green

Hedged round with privet
As with habit and with age,
Move the bowlers
On the lawn that is their stage.

Their gestures inflame the air
Like impatient clouds
Gathering to some point far away
That the sunset shrouds

And weighs with red.
The arm swings forward while the eye
Is calm that contemplates the speed.
Marvellous, the silent rounded cry

Of motion, ending
In collision.
Then come measuring-tapes,
Disagreement and confusion.

Is this Olympus where the Gods
Spin the dark planets, holding fate
In hands tobacco-stained?
Or can they only hope the bowl runs straight?

Lucy Barker (17)
James Allen's Girls' School,
Dulwich, London
(Gold Medal Award winner)

Weather Forecast

The wind

'Help!' say the trees
as it blows down the branches
and tosses up leaves.
'Help!' say I as I struggle to school
trying to stay on my feet.
'Help!' says my mum chasing the dustbin
that rolls down the street.
'Hurray,' shouts the boy whose kite flies high
Soaring and diving up into the sky.

Kirsty Topping (7)
Linlithgow Primary School,
Linlithgow, West Lothian

The weather forecast

'It may rain tomorrow,'
The man on the radio said.
'It may rain tomorrow
'While you're in bed.'

We're off to the seaside tomorrow,
At least that's what Dad said.
But if it rains tomorrow
We'll stay at home instead.

I hope that it rains when I'm sleeping
Like the man on the radio said.
I hope that it rains while I'm sleeping
Snug and warm in my bed.

I hope that the sun shines tomorrow,
While we're at the seaside as Dad said.
I hope that the sun shines tomorrow,
So we don't have to stay home instead.

The morning has come and it's sunny.
It rained while I was in bed.
So we're off to the seaside this day,
So blow what the weather man said.

Charles Talbot (8)
St Andrew's School,
Rochester, Kent

I can't take the sun

I can't take the sun no more, Man.
I buy fifty cans of cola,
I take my clothes off,
But I'm still hot.
I might as well take off my skin
It's so so so so hot, Man.
I just can't take the sun no more.
I might as well take myself apart
Before the sun melts me.
It's so so so so so so so so so
Hot, Man.
Just can't take the sun, Man.

Linval Quinland (10)
Grasmere Primary School,
Stoke Newington, London

'Swimmers'
Andrew Hunt (11)
Sir Hugh Owen Lower School
Caernarfon, Gwynedd

The igloo

As I smashed the ice
Pieces flew from the ground
Like fragments of glass.
The cold wind howled.

Slicing the ice,
Enormous blocks,
I struggled.
Snow crunched under my feet.

I balanced the blocks
My hands were numb.
The igloo was nearly built.
I went inside.

A few more blocks.
It was finished.
I crawled in.
I made a fire.

The fire was glowing.
There inside it was warm,
Sparks were flying.
I drifted to sleep.

Clarissa Landcastle (9)
Treorchy Comprehensive School,
Treorchy, Rhondda,
Mid Glamorgan

Wind

I love the wind,
The wind blows me,
It is shivery and freezing,
Setting me free.

James Challis (5)
Foxhole Infants' School,
Paignton, Devon

February looking outdoors

The silver moon shines bright
Like a sapphire still at night.
The trickling water
Runs down the silky leaves
And the snowflakes fall like lace.
An eagle rises up to a golden nest
While the beautiful white flock of
   swans
Flap their wings slowly.

Lucy Hawes (7)
Wheatley Primary School,
Wheatley, Oxfordshire

It's raining

Rain is wet
Annoying
It tickled my sister
She laughed
It tickled me too.

Jessica Slattery (7)
St Michael on the
Mount CE
Primary School,
Bristol, Avon

Storm

A storm is a fox,
darting, leaping.
His tail is lightning.
His foot is thunder.

Danny Manning (7)
Grasmere Primary
School,
Stoke Newington,
London

The rainbow

When the rain and the sun,
Are battling it out
To see who can last the longest
The rainbow comes out
And settles it.

Rachel Ludkin (10)
Canon Pickering Junior School,
Harleston, Norfolk

'Study of Horses'
Mohammed Ajmal (14)
Eastcliffe Grammar School
Gosforth, Newcastle Upon Tyne

The wind

The wind creeps around dustbins and
  disturbs them,
The wind digs in dirty rubbish
  looking for useful things.

Millions of invisible ants pick up
  the rubbish and take it to their
  leader in the corner of the
  playground.

The wind picks up the rubbish to go
  to a ball and dance with it,
But the sun army comes out.
The wind army battles with the sun
  army,
There is clattering of cold and hot
  swords.
The sun army wins because it is too
  hot.

The wind jumps into the sea.
Now the sun is smiling.

Douglas Bridges (7)
Meridian County Primary School,
Peacehaven, East Sussex

The gale

The gale came
It rained and rained
I was blown into school
my trousers were wet
I had to wear PE shorts.
The tiles blew down
the builders couldn't work
rubbish blew off the skip
We all watched the gale from the classroom window.
When we came home the slide had blown off
the fence was down
but the rabbit was safe in his hutch.

Tom Forster (6)
Sedbury,
Chepstow, Gwent

'At the End of the
Street Was the
Church'
John Sharp (10)
Dulwich College
Prep School
Cranbrook, Kent

Light, Bright and Beautiful

Power cut

The lights went off
The kitchen looked spooky in the gloom and dark
Mummy stood on a chair
And opened the cupboard
Out came the candles
I put the candles in the candle holders
I struck a match
The candles were lit
It looked beautiful
When the lights came on again
I felt sad

Paul Forster (6)
Sedbury,
Chepstow, Gwent

Electricity

I am electricity.
I go through the
land invisibly
into everything.

Rebecca Hughes (5)
St Catherine's School,
Camberley, Surrey
(Silver Medal Award
winner)

The star

I'm the star who shines so bright
Who led the three kings into the night.
I tear the sky.
I leap in the air.
I shine extra bright.
I am always there.
I light up in the dark black sky.
I'm always there floating by.
The night comes again,
I shine so bright
I'll lead you anywhere in the night.
Just wish for me and I'll be there.
I'm always here in the air.

Alice Usiskin (10)
Greycotes School,
Oxford

Rockets

A match alight
A rocket racing into the air
And coming down in
rainbows of rage

Jonathan Brown (7)
St Erth County Primary
School,
Hayle, Cornwall

Hall of mirrors

Colour glistens and darts around
Hall of Mirrors where reflections live,
Shadows surprise, reflections revive
You multiplied a hundred times
You divided a hundred times
All of you stares back at you
Split in half, and hanged and quartered,
Staring hard, frowning back,
Colour rushes round the room,
Faster than light, louder than sound,
And so strangely
Confuses confusion.

Timothy Waters (9)
University College Junior School,
Hampstead, London

Bubbles

When you blow the
bubbles they wobble out
Like fat rain floating sideways.
When you hold your hand out
sometimes they bounce up and
down until they fade away.
They look like a soft glass ball.
When they fall they leave behind water prints.
It looks like bubbles have got
windows with colours.
Green, purple, blue and white.
They float around looking wobbly and silvery.

Ryan Goad (7)
Lincewood Junior School,
Basildon, Essex

'Singer'
Sam Mortan (17)
Ysgol Gyfun Emlyn
New Castle Emlyn, Dyfed

137

HAIKU: Japanese garden

Stepping stones are firm.
They stand there in the water
While the water runs.

Nicola Forster (7)
Whalley CE Primary School,
Whalley, Lancashire

The pillar box

The pillar box is fat and red
Its mouth is open wide
It wears a tammy on its head
It must be dark inside

Nicola Price (9)
Washacre County Primary
School,
Westhoughton, Bolton,
Lancashire

Ways of looking at a flower

1
There is a flower
in the
field with
lots of other
flowers.

2
There is a flower
in a jug on
its own
with no other
flowers
around it.

3
There is a
jug with
lots of other
flowers
in it too.

4
Ten flowers
in a jug, all
different colours.

5
There are no flowers
in the jug,
they are on the table
waiting to be put
in water.

6
There are ten
flowers waiting
to be put in
water.

7
There are no flowers
in the jug
and no flowers
in the field.

8
Have you seen
that
beautiful flower in
the jug?

9
There are no
flowers
in the jug or
in the house.

10
Today I have
seen no flowers
in the house
in the field
or on the table.

Racheal Cuncarr (9)
Whalley CE Primary
School,
Whalley, Lancashire

Dancing daffodil

Dancing daffodil standing alone,
Along came a daffodil and said,
  do a dance for me.
First I need some wind
Flowing on my petals
Over the leaves
Dance with me please
In the sunlight with me
Little dancing daffodil
  dance with me.

Nicholas Conway (9) and Noel
Midgeley (10)
Woodroyd Middle School,
West Bowling, Bradford,
West Yorkshire

'Self Portrait'
Sally Ross (16)
Albyn School For Girls
Aberdeen

Thoughts of a seed

A little boy planted me;
   I feel cool and safe in the soil
   As black as dark.
   I'm thirsty now.
   Who will give me a drink?
   Here comes the rain.
When I push through the soil
   It will be hard,
As hard as a bone.
   I want to grow
   Into a sunflower, yellow bright.
   I want to grow
   Up, as high as the clouds.
Then the wind can blow
   And bend me;
My seeds will scatter
   And the little boy can eat them.
   They tell me I need light to grow.
I hope nobody switches off the light.

Ben Thackeray (4), Andrew Pimblott (4),
Paul Armstrong (5), Lauren Eves (5),
Roger Twiss (4), David Cross (4) and
Richard Jones (4)
Ysgol Penmorfa,
Prestatyn, Clwyd

Rhubarb

I'm a little stick of rhubarb,
In a garden rhubarb bed,
With a load of muck around me roots,
And a bucket on me head.

It must be nearly spring outside,
But how can I tell.
I haven't heard the cuckoo yet,
In here it's as black as hell.

They say that all the snow has gone,
And everything is growing.
Weeds are coming up a treat,
And the grass will soon need mowing.

And then they'll come and look at me,
Shift the bucket off me head.
Shake all the muck from around me roots.
And pour custard on instead.

Benjamin Porter-Jones (14)
Callington Community School,
Callington, Cornwall

To a snake's-head fritillary

A piece of over-wrought confectionery,
Concocted by some Marie-Antoinette
Or nature-preacher by a study fire:
Keen but over-theoretical.

Once opened, the flower never blinks,
Seeing nothing, never flinches.

The stem discreetly does the work,
But of what purpose is the bloom?

Mere bees cannot conceive its special poise,
Its courage in the face of cosmic blue.

It stores its seeds like memoirs in the earth
(That filing-cabinet of future life),
From which will issue forth one distant spring
Shoots to sing the life-song once again.

Lucy Barker (17)
James Allen's Girls' School,
Dulwich, London
(Gold Medal Award winner)

Bradwell

The Roman road.
Is dusty and stony.
We march as Roman soldiers
To the giant grey fort of Othona
On either side there is seed rape,
The flowers are pale yellow
As they grow in the middle of nowhere
The trees are leafless and
   dead.
Ivy grows up the strangled trunks.
In the distance an isolated church
Stands out on the horizon.
Skylarks sing sweetly
As they hover and soar
Into the grey, rain-filled clouds.

Sarah Webb (7)
St Cedd's School,
Chelmsford, Essex

Magic and Mystery

The room's ghost

Her bony fingers run down the arm of the chair,
The long nails scratching the wood;
Her hair like cobwebs and her body dust
Floating across the floor.
She does not leave footprints . . .
The dust moves, then settles again.
The moth-eaten curtains blow in and out of the open
    window,
And as she touches them,
They crumble.

The scentless pot-pourri
Has a frosted edge,
Frosted with dust and cobwebs.
She is so beautiful with her hair of cobwebs
And her body of dust.
The room she lives in is dark and gloomy,
With only a shaft of sunlight
Peeping through the curtains.
But the rays will never warm her again.

Gemma White (10)
Halesworth Middle School,
Halesworth, Suffolk

Gremlin

In the darkness . . .
On the window sill
A gremlin . . . lurks.
Shunts across the room.
I freeze
. . . Mu . . Mu . . . Mum!

Patrick Waterhouse (7)
Swainswick CE Primary
School,
Upper Swainswick, Bath,
Avon

'Dinosaur
Tyrannosaurus'
Jessie Nesbit (7)
Miles Coverdale School
London
(Silver Medal Award
winner)

It's dark now

It's dark now,
but really I'm not scared!
Sometimes I think of ghosts
but I always know it's just my imagination
Ghosts don't exist though,
Do they?
I hear a shimmering noise
in the hall
A shadowy figure
floats by my bedroom.
I clutch my favourite blanket
I cannot scream,
I seem to have lost my voice.
I tear my favourite blanket in half.
Mum suddenly bursts in and says . . .
'Are you still up, and you've torn your nice blanket.'

Sanjay Joshi (7)
Cambridge

Dream of a wolf

Night,
Just before sleep
Lays its thick blankets
Over my brain,
I whisper to my pillow
'Please,
Please let me sleep
In peace tonight.'
But yet again,
As I close my eyes,
I find myself
Back
In that seemingly
Ordinary
Classroom,
Surrounded by seemingly
Ordinary
Children,
But wait,
Take a look out of the window,
It is a lone classroom.
All by itself,
In a vast expanse of white.
Snowflakes softly drop,
As the fat teacher begins to
Preach her sermon
In a low droning voice.
Then,
Another noise breaks the monotony.
A howl,
A long drawn-out wolf's howl.

The melancholy wail is joined
By Another,
And Another,
Until the whole world seems
Bursting
With the noise.

But the lesson continues.
Surely the fat teacher has heard
The wolf's desperate
Howl?
But no, the lesson continues.

I glance uneasily out
Of the window.
I stare hard,
But my anxious eyes
Can detect nothing
But the snow,
The strange snow
That sparkles like champagne.

Then a small piece of pink
Paper,
Small and insignificant
Gets caught
By a sudden gust of insolent
Wind.
It is flung
By the breeze
And tossed out of the
Open door
To land, with a rustle
On the white carpet outside.

It seems to grin at the teacher,
Who,
Vexed by this unwelcome
Interruption
Heaves herself up, out of
Her throne,
And waddles to the door,
Like a fattened duck.

I can see what will happen,
But
As I try to scream
'No!'
The words cannot force themselves
From my numbed
Lips.
She walks out,
The snowflakes quietly
Descending on her hair and shoulders.
She walks
Further and
Further
Away from the safety
Of the solitary classroom,
On and on
To where the paper sits,
Temptingly, still grinning
On the white blanket.
She reaches for
The pink scrap
Of triviality
And stops.

She bends down
To pick it up.
While
She bends,
As if in slow motion
A huge grey wolf
Bounds into sight,
Licks its lips,
Obscenely,
Pants,
Then runs for that
Helpless
Figure in the snow.

She stands up
Slowly,
And stares the apparition
Full in the face.

For a minute,
She cannot comprehend.
Then scream after scream
Tears the air into shreds
That fly around like shrapnel
Into our horrified faces.

Then, the class
Of ordinary children
Get up
And, like robots
File out of that
Dreadful door.

My limbs no longer
Obey me,
And I am the last to rise.
We walk
Out of our haven
To certain death.
And for each child
There is a wolf
Waiting,
Its eyes hungry,
Its jaws
Dripping.
The grey wolf
Looks up for a moment,
As if to smile,
Then continues tearing the
Pathetic lifeless bundle.

The white becomes splashed
With red
And as I walk through
The door, I know
What is to come.
Now I step out
Into the brilliant white snow,
And see a wolf
Staring at me.

Shaggy and black
Its red eyes blazing with hate,
It lunges for me.
I back away,
But the snow hinders my steps.

It is upon me,
Rearing,
Its paws are on my shoulders
Pushing me down, down.

I can feel its hot, foul,
Death-tainted breath
On my cheeks.
I'm pushed over,
Crushed
By its great weight.
I see its gleaming fangs
And it seems to sneer at me
Before it lunges.
I feel a searing pain
As its teeth slice into
My delicate throat flesh.
Now my blood stains the snow.
Scream after tortured scream
Erupt from my mouth,
Then die
To a dry gurgle.
The white hot pain
Seems to last
Forever
The world goes red
White,
Black.
I am dead.

But not so,
My eyes open quickly
And search for something
Comforting.

My chest heaves,
I am
Back
In my bed.
Light streams through the
Gaps in the curtains,
And
In the distance
A black bird sings
'How do you do do?
'How do you do do?'
For me, the world
Is full
Of joy again.

Nilmini de Silva (16)
Swindon, Wiltshire

'Mountains of the Moon'
Georgina Hucker (11)
Halesworth Middle School
Halesworth, Suffolk

A spell for intelligence

Take dolphin's brain and rabbit's foot,
Wombat's toe and mandrake root;
Add herb and spice of garlic rue,
Bits of soot from up the flue;
Add tooth of frog and tongue of bat,
Bits of this and bits of that;
Add cobra's blood and python's scale,
Ivory from a hump-backed whale;
Add frog's legs, toad's eyes, and a large bat;
(You must remember all of that);
Stir it round for a first time,
Put in two large leaves of lime;
Add dragon's hair and squoodle's knee,
(For those you go on a good long spree!);
There will be an enormous flash,
Dip a spoon in with a splash;
Take five spoons of this concoction;
And you'll be intelligent – NO option!

Hamish Symington (9)
St Andrew's School,
Meads, Eastbourne,
East Sussex

Japanese tea house

The lonely tea house,
Stands alone,
No one to take care of it,
No one to talk to it,
Be kind to it;
Watching itself fall to pieces,
Watching the sun rise and set,

Watching the moon come and go,

But it is still standing there,
All alone.

The stream floats past

The tea house,
Just soaking,
Into its soul.

Rebecca Seery (7)
Whalley CE Primary School,
Whalley, Lancashire

My robot

My robot is made of cogs and wheels.
Metal and springs.
Sparkling eyes and grabbing claws.
Nuts and screws.
Shaking shivering iron jaws.
Squeaking creaking iron arms.
Bolted nose and gleaming gold teeth.
Dials wires and brass mouth.
When he talks his voice is
   flat.
He calls 'More oil, more oil, more oil.'

Rachel Games (7)
Fernhill Manor Junior School,
New Milton, Hampshire

'Deck of Cards'
Group work (15)
Hereford School
Grimsby, South Humberside
(Silver Medal Award winner)

The leader of creation

From the black darkness a light flew with a white
 shimmer,
Something moved with the twist of a magic horn,
The leader, the unicorn of light appeared,
His wings as white as light and horn filled with mystery,
Thundering the skies as he flew,
He was creating a new world,
Making a new light,
From the dark he made light,
And on earth he made living things,
He made his kingdom for them as a new world,
But the greatest thing he made was horse,
He gave us power of all creatures,
He gave us speed and freedom to be wild.

Sophie Bonas (10)
St Catherine's School,
Camberley, Surrey

The ancient one

The ancient one
so
cold but sweet.
Deer
birds and owls
live
on him for
woodland
is most of his
life.
He is the keeper
of
All the forest,
The Ancient One
so
cold but sweet,
keeper
of life, keeper
of
all goodness, but
he
keeps out badness
and
harm.
The Ancient One
so
cold and sweet,
keeper
of all the forest.

Victoria Tomlinson (10)
Whalley CE Primary
School,
Whalley, Lancashire

Conflict

Conflict

The comb ran smoothly through my slicked-back hair
As I stood back and took a look in the mirror.
Wow.
It was almost time: five to the hour.
I crept down the stairs,
Carefully avoiding the kitchen,
And gently, ever so gently, opened the back door.
It was oiled.
That was good.
As the latch dropped with a silent click
I felt a twinge of nerves in my stomach.
This was it.

Quickly but carefully, I tiptoed round the back of the
    house,
Past the vegetables
Opposite the rabbit hutch.
It was all going perfectly.

'Salim?'
I darted round and stared back at the house,
Frozen to the spot.
MY GOD, WHAT NOW?
I stood there, my muscles aching with the tension.
'Salim? Are you coming down?
'Salim?'
She's not going to stop,
She'll go on and on, on and on.
Father is due back late.

The small red Renault drew up the drive.
No.
NO!
It's not him!

It was him.

'Salim's not in his room! He's gone!'
I heard my mother shriek at my father.
'He's not there!'
She screamed, a terrifying scream;
It made me sick: this just wasn't happening.

I slowly walked back to the house,
Not bothering to tiptoe now.
I pushed open the door effortlessly,
Yet with an unbearable strain.
Father was there with mother, lying on the sofa.
He jerked quickly as he heard the door click shut.

'Salim. What the hell do you think you're playing at?'
I tensed my body as he came towards me.
He yanked my arm and pushed me into a chair.
'What is all this hair gel and fancy clothes?
'Where did you get those?'
'Father, I – It was just –'
'Just what?'
'There's this girl –'
'What? Did you say "girl"?'
'Father, please.'
'I've told you before. You know how we feel.'
'But fath –'
'Enough buts. Your wife will be chosen for you. You
  know that.'
'Yes father.'
'If it happens again, no longer will you be welcome in
                                        this household

Now get to your room!'

Kieron Mohindra (14)
The King's School,
Canterbury, Kent
(Special Mention)

Hate . . .

I stood frozen by the harsh words,
of hate,
'I'm going John, I'm going.' They
echoed in my mind,
'I'm going John, I'm going . . .'

The hurried sound of packing,
the slam of a door and my life
was thrown upside down.
Bitter tears rolled down my face and
dripped on to my nightdress, Mum!

'She'll be back,' he snapped.
I hated him.
He drove my mother away like a
stranger,
Verbally attacking her every minute
of the day
until,
no more words could be spoken, no
more abuse could be taken.
He pushed her
out of my
life and
I hated him.
                                        I really hated him.

Susannah Fish (13)
Wymondham High School,
Wymondham, Norfolk

My bird Peter

My bird was yellow,
And my brother killed it.
It is in our back garden,
And it was gorgeous.

And I want it,
Because I liked it,
Because it was my bird.
It could stand on the tele.
It was funny.
It did do funny things.

Then it did love my mummy.

When it died it was only five.
Our David did not like it,
Because his tail kept going in his nose.
So he got this knife and he stabbed it.

I battered him.
I kicked him in the leg.
Me and my mum went to the pet shop,
And we will get another one next week.

Sarah Taylor (6)
St Margaret's C of E Infant School,
Orford, Warrington,
Cheshire

That was not here

Perhaps somewhere, on some battlefield,
The soldiers stride along,
Their minds alert, their bodies fit,
Their voices raised in song.

But that was not here, was not this battlefield,
Was not Passchendaele where men stumbled and stared
Wild-eyed, through masks of blood
And dropped, screaming in agony, falling to roll over and
    over
Until, at last,
They lay still.

That was not here, was not this hell
Where the bodies of friends and comrades
Lay sprawled where they fell, piled up against the walls
    of the trenches
As bait for the rats – sacrificing themselves even in death –
To keep us alive
For another hour.

That was not here, not in this place,
Ploughing knee-deep through the sea of putrefying flesh
Half-recognizing here a face, there an expression,
Amongst the decaying remains of the pride of England.
What mother would do this to her sons? I asked myself,
My stomach churning as I stumbled over a wounded ally
    sprawled in the slime.
His eyes locked with mine, pleadingly, and his imploring
    hands reached out
As if to welcome the bullet
From my rifle.

On reaching the trenches and turning to look back at the
  battlefield,
Something shimmering, faintly coloured in the twilight,
Caught my eye.
I'd left something behind; trampled into the mud
Of Passchendaele –
A faded, fragmented, forgotten fantasy;
A dream of glory.

Hilary Davies (14)
Wellington School,
Carleton Turrets, Ayr

Flutter

Walk in.
Walk out.
Leave the door swinging.
No knock.
No bell.
No warning.
An entry.
An exit.
Eyes focused.
The door dies on the draught
that shook your shattering world.

Claire Ginn (17)
Billericay School,
Billericay, Essex

My mum's father

In Finland,
Before I was born,
My mum's father,
Hid most of his weapons,
In the cellar,
At the bottom of the house.
Some people,
Found out.
He was taken as a prisoner,
And a few weeks later,
He was set free again,
And he died the year after.
My grandmother has a picture,
Of my grandad,
And I cry,
Every time,
I look at it.

Lucy Golding (7)
St Cedd's School,
Chelmsford, Essex
(Silver Medal Award winner)

Death in the trap

Where's the castle with the mountain?
The sea round where the man died?
In a trap in a trap.
His remains are only his skin.
The people of the village took him to the pond.
Threw him in.
Covered the pond with silk.

Christopher Pattle (6)
Eynesbury CE School,
St Neot's, Cambridgeshire

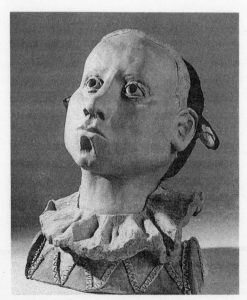

'Head'
Gillian Lang (16)
Holyrood Secondary
School
Glasgow

Silver dream

His was
A silver dream of peace,
Equality for men,
No black or white,
Just silver;
No rioting again.

One voice
Shouted out from the mumble,
One voice
To set wrongs right;
One voice
With a million echoes,
The voice of
Martin Luther King.

One leaden mind,
One leaden fist,
One leaden trigger pulled,
One leaden bullet
Glinting death
Slashed against the dreamer.

The silver melted
To a poppy red
Then hardened to black mourning,
Tarnished silver
Ridden with grief,
With protests
And with rioting.

Inspired by the dream,
New silver came,
New wisdom and rejoicing;
The silver dreamer may have died
But the dream lives on
Still shining.

Tony Roberts (13)
Debenham High School,
Debenham, Stowmarket,
Suffolk

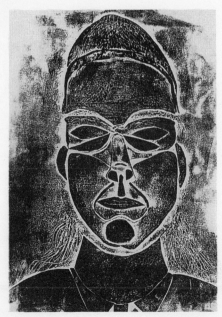

'Myself'
Minal Shah (12)
Woodford County High
School
Woodford Green, Essex

There were no potatoes

There were no potatoes.
The woman in the middle of the
    queue,
Stamped her feet,
To keep out the chill.
The frost crunched in the square,
Under the heavy boots of the
    soldiers.
A man walked into the church,
The vaulted ceiling high above,
He thought of days gone by,
The clear air carried the bite of
    winter,
A child threw a snowball,
Into the air,
He wandered through the city
    streets.
A scrawny cat whined.
He made his way into the square.
The woman in the queue,
Envied his innocence.
He stopped to pull the arm of a
    soldier.
The soldier shrugged him off with
    a smile.
The child of a poor world,
Surrounded by riches.

The golden domes stood in the sky,
A symbol of equality and death,
They glittered in the cold light.
Inside men worked,
To make the world a better place,
A country for the children.
Great plans,
Of reform and revolution,
Loosening bonds,
Strengthening ties.
Improving the houses,
Stopping the killing in the
    streets,
Giving the right to hear,
And to be heard,
The grand design,
A country fit for heroes,
A jewel in the world of men.
One man,
Risking his life for the people,
Giving them another chance,
A better way,
And there were still no potatoes.

James Wolfe (13)
Garendon High School,
Loughborough, Leicestershire

Media man

He pans the crowd,
Sees the one man,
Points the camera
And releases the shutter.
The image is imprinted
On the silver
Of film.

The negative brightens
The dark of the room.
Shapes begin to focus
In the tray of chemicals.
That single petrol bomb
In one man's hand
Stands out,
Enlarged

So the people see
What is really happening.

Tim Connors (13)
Debenham High School,
Debenham, Stowmarket,
Suffolk

Question Marks

Look

I
  wonder
        what
           it's
             like
               to
                be
                  you
                    and
                    look
                   at
                 me
             from
         your
       point
     of
view!   *Emily Douglas (11)*
               Yate, Bristol,
               Avon

A riddle

I was the downfall of Adam,
The temptation of Eve
I gave Newton inspiration,
And am grown on trees
I was the founder of science,
And discovered gravity
I am found near Table Mountain,
And also in Paris
I can be alcoholic,
But normally am sweet
My Granny's name is Smith,
And her husband is Toffee

I'm big in New York,
And common in pie
I go well with pork,
And drop from the sky
I have a son, Cox
And a daughter, Pippin
Am popular with snakes,
Who created sin

By now you will have guessed my true identity:
    Cox 'Pippin' Apple

I'm sure that you now see.

Neil Daugherty (11)
Tylers Green County Middle School,
Tylers Green, Buckinghamshire

What's in a poem?

'What's in a poem?'
My brother asked one day
'Although it isn't difficult
'I don't know what to say.'

'Oh! It's just imagination
'With a bit of inspiration,
'And a little application
It's a rhyme and time sensation!'

?

!

Nana Francois (9)
Summertown,
Oxford

A word to Bros

Bros, my dear fellows,
Can't you see you CAN'T sing?
Your attitude's deplorable,
And your fans make such a din!

Amanda Bateson (14)
Dudley, Cramlington,
Northumberland

Adults

I don't really understand adults,
They may be quite clever, it's true.
They may know their tables word perfect,
Which is better than most kids can do.

Yet sometimes when they need assistance,
And we cannot be reached by a call,
Instead of facing the bother of fetching us,
They themselves do it all.

It's funny to watch at a friend's house,
How when we finally sit down for tea,
The parents have little competitions,
To see how polite they can tell us to be.

I definitely don't understand adults,
So when my childhood's gone,
I wonder how then I'll see adults,
And if I'll understand them when I am one.

Karen Knocker (10)
Golden Valley Primary School,
Nailsea, Avon

Jeremy, where's your father?

Jeremy, where's your father?
Why must they ask me?
They only do it to annoy
and because they know where he is
The teachers aren't much help either,
Write about a family outing . . .
Write about your family tree
Or in maths
If your mother gives you £2.50
and your father gives you. . .oh, sorry Jeremy
Wish they'd shut up about their fathers.
Philip's is a bank manager
Jen's is a teacher at another school.
Pete hardly sees his.
He's away a lot
On business trips
Matthew's are divorced.
At least that's respectable.
Everyone knows where my father is.
Ten years.
I'll be twenty-two by the time he's out.
Wish they'd stop talking about it,
it's not as if it's my fault.
Nobody seems to see I don't find it funny
when they laugh and smile secretly at each other
and ask me
Where's your father, Jeremy?

Sarah Todd (16)
Penparcau, Aberystwyth,
Dyfed

Why the elephant?

Why me?
Is it because my ears are too big?
But there again, monkeys have big ears too.

Why me?
Is it because we have big feet?
But there again, bears have big feet too.

Why me?
Is it because I make holes in the ground?
But there again, diggers make holes in the ground too.

Why me?
Is it the noise I make?
But there again, tractors make noise too.

Is it because of my trunk?
But people use hosepipes.

I don't understand.
Why me?

Paul Woodger (7)
St George's CP School, Wrotham,
Sevenoaks, Kent

Tell him

His childish brown eyes,
They'll look at me from his cocked head,
Those innocent eyes,
Wide with disbelief.

I'll have to say it a third,
Maybe fourth time before he'll understand,
It's not a game
I'm not playing now.

He'll grasp for alternatives.
He'll tell me he doesn't mind.
He can stand it.
Anything to stop me.

He'll cry
He'll laugh
He'll even propose to me,
God knows what he'll do.

I can't mother him any more
I can't come to reassure him and tell him it's all right
Because it isn't.
It's all wrong.

What will it be like without his outstretched arms
And his boyish grin to welcome me
And his soft smile
As he whispers 'Goodnight' in my ear?

How will I tell him?
How can I tell him?
Why should I tell him?
After all
I love him.

Anna Imber (11)
Marden Bridge Middle School,
Whitley Bay, North Tyneside

They hadn't known . . .

They hadn't known that things would be like this;
Dawn broke now without the glorious singing of the
   rising lark,
Dusk fell without the wistful song of the nightingale.
Little did they realize their loss.
No longer would the sight of soaring eagles
Catch an earnest watcher's breath.
Nor a homely wren alighting on a sill
Send a small boy into ecstasy.
None were spared; neither harmless dove nor faithful
   robin.
Even the most slovenly nest – a treasured relic.
And the mockingbird will mock no more.

They hadn't known that things would be like this;
No hedgehog rustling through rusty leaves,
Or noble horses neighing.
No longer woken by cunning foxes scavenging.
Headlights ceased to catch the glint of timid rabbits'
   eyes.
Wild – today an unused word –
Unless a new meaning can be found.
Our future generations will forgo pleasures
Of observing a faint butterfly emerging,
And a spotted lady ascending to faltering heights.
And the bees will hum no more.

They hadn't known that things would be like this;
No sunflowers reaching for the glaring sun,
Or clumps of trees casting long, dark shadows.
Not a tinkling tuft of grass burst forth.
Rosy, heart-shaped fruits, forgotten,
No freshly cut fragrances in a vase.
Such similes as 'cool as a cucumber' and 'as agile as a
    monkey'
Will perplex our heirs.
What reaction will be revealed,
When searching voices enquire 'What is an animal?'
And the grass is green no more.

I ask myself
Why?
How did this happen?
Man's thoughtlessness can be the only answer.
For want and greed,
Unsatisfied with possession,
Always wanting one thing more.
Irreversible damage has supervened.
Plants, birds, animals – words of the past
One great caterpillar track bulldozed through the
    countryside,
Little thought for the future.
The whole world has become one gigantic trading estate.
This planet, a huge rubbish tip,
An enoromous black hole, from which we cannot escape.
And they said they didn't know . . .

Rebecca Morris (16)
St David's School, Wrexham,
Clwyd

I am a child

I am a child from a Vietnamese city
In a Hong Kong refugee camp,
Cramped and uncomfortable,
But I can't go back home.
Unwanted, unloved, homeless,
I'm growing up without a future.
Why do we have to live like this?

I am a child in a Brazilian forest.
The gold-diggers are endangering our lives.
They're bringing disease
And polluting the rivers.
The trees have been burned
And the landscape ruined.
Why are they doing this?

I am a child, a Romanian orphan.
I have no-one to kiss goodnight.
My bed is cold, my blanket is thin
And my old, worn teddy is not here to hug.
I miss my friends,
And my brothers and sisters.
Oh where are they all now?

I am a child growing up in Ulster,
Soldiers with guns on every street,
Terrorists with bombs,
Buses burning.
Was that a gun or did a car backfire?
Afraid of the darkness.
Will my dad come home tonight?

I am a child in a London doorway,
Cold and lonely, begging for food,
Sleeping in boxes,
No one to love me,
Hiding from view,
Tired and wet.
Who can I trust and who will harm me?

I am a child in a Lancashire village,
Beautiful clothes and plenty to eat,
A room full of toys,
A home full of happiness,
A mum and dad who care,
Happy and contented,
But what does the future hold?

Leah Smith (10)
Whalley CE Primary School,
Whalley, Lancashire

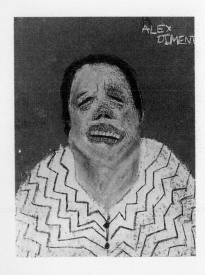

'Charcoal Portrait'
Alexander Diment (11)
Cumnor House School
Haywards Heath, East Sussex

185

The 1991 Cadbury's Poetry Competition

The Cadbury's Books of Children's Poetry contain about 160 selected entries from children of all ages and are illustrated with work from the National Exhibition of Children's Art.

If you would like to enter the 1991 competition whether in the Art & Design or Poetry sections, you can write to this address for an entry form:

Cadbury's National Exhibition of Children's Art
Granby
Altrincham
Cheshire
WA14 5SZ

(Please enclose a stamped/addressed envelope)

Remember–you may win a chance to feature in the *Cadbury's Ninth Book of Children's Poetry*.

Index of titles

Index of authors